Education/Mathematics: a second-level course
EM236   Learning and Teaching Mathematics

Teaching Mathematics:
Action and Awareness

Prepared by Eric Love and John Mason for the course team

The Open University

Acknowledgements

Grateful acknowledgement is made to the following source for permission to reproduce material in this text:

Figures

p. 8: Giles, G. (1984), *Number patterns 1 – Simple Mappings*, DIME Projects, Stirling; p. 9: 'More matchstick patterns', School Mathematics Project (SMP), (1983), *Formulas: Extension 1*, SMP 11–16, Cambridge University Press; p. 13: Bell, A., Wigley, D. and Rooke, D. (1978), *Journey into Maths: Teacher's Guide 1*, Shell Centre, University of Nottingham.

The Open University, Walton Hall, Milton Keynes, MK7 6AA

First published 1992

Designed by the Graphic Design Group of the Open University

Printed in the United Kingdom by Hobbs the Printers Ltd,
Second Avenue, Southampton, SO9 2UZ

ISBN 0 7492 3070 3

This monograph forms part of an Open University course. If you have not enrolled on the course and would like to buy this or other Open University material, please write to Open University Educational Enterprises Ltd, 12 Cofferidge Close, Stony Stratford, MK11 1BY. If you wish to enquire about enrolling as an Open University student, please write to The Admissions Office, The Open University, PO Box 48, Walton Hall, Milton Keynes, MK7 6AB.

1.1

Contents

Prologue

Teaching mathematics is a peculiar business. It requires the teacher to act at some times and to appear not to act at others; to respond or intervene at some times, and to hold back, observe or even go away at others, so that pupils can discover what they can do for themselves. But any statements about teaching, including the previous sentence, reflect attitudes, beliefs and perceptions about mathematics, about teaching, and about learning.

No matter how much educational legislation is passed, no matter how many directives are issued from outside and inside the school, in the final analysis teachers construct the curriculum for their pupils. They choose what pupils will do and, through the actions that they take, they influence how the pupils work. They construct the curriculum from schemes and workcards, from ideas derived from colleagues and from their own insights, all informed by attainment targets and other statutory and non-statutory governmental guidance. Two teachers using the same scheme, even the same apparatus, will conduct quite different lessons because they differ in their views of mathematics and its place in the whole curriculum, in their beliefs about how children learn, and in how they manifest their own mathematical thinking in the classroom.

There are many different teacher actions:

> proposing tasks;
>
> asking questions;
>
> telling pupils things;
>
> initiating discussion;
>
> commenting on work;
>
> evaluating;
>
> urging pupils to practise to automate techniques; …

In proposing a mathematical task, teachers have a sense of what they want or expect the pupils to do with it and get from it. They are aware of what aspects they intend to stress, and where it fits into the work of the day, term, year, as well as into any legislated description such as a national curriculum.* What makes one teacher stress one aspect and a second stress another? How do pupils work out what is expected of them? How do the teachers in a school communicate about what they expect to happen among themselves?

Messages about mathematics, about its role and value in society and about how it is learned, are implicit in the ways that actions are carried out. And these are influenced by views of mathematics itself. Mathematics can be seen as a body of knowledge to be handed over to the next generation (from which comes the metaphor of *delivering the curriculum* like some mail-order package) and it can be seen as a process of disciplined inquiry and analysis (from which comes the

---

* The term 'a national curriculum' is used to refer to relevant legislation such as that in England and Wales, Scotland and Northern Ireland.

metaphor of *exploring and investigating*). Both views (and there are many variants) have an element of fit but when one view is elevated to *the* view of mathematics it leads to imbalance and impoverishment for pupils. Having an active, exploratory, investigative approach to mathematics does not guarantee that pupils will take pleasure in exploration and gain confidence with mathematics, just as an approach based on 'exposition-example-practice' does not guarantee that all pupils will succeed or even that all will struggle constructively.

Mathematics teaching involves taking actions in classrooms in order to prompt pupils to act on:

- physical objects by manipulating them (Dienes blocks, attribute blocks, Cuisenaire or colour factor rods, counters, shells and beads, compasses, protractors, rulers, calculators, and so on);
- screen objects (images on computer screens, television, posters);
- symbols (numerals, variables, labels, words);
- mental objects (pictures-in-the-head, vague senses, intuitions).

Often the action is precipitated by getting pupils to express their thinking to themselves, to other pupils, to the teacher, and to examiners, via talking, writing, drawing, computer programs, audio and videotapes, and drama.

This complex range of possibilities is too big a subject to be dealt with comprehensively in this monograph. Our aim is modest: firstly, we point out some common views about mathematics, about teaching and about mathematical activity and how these may influence what happens in classrooms. Secondly, we propose some distinctions for probing beneath the intentions behind current and possible actions. Our concern here is both with the choice of tasks for pupils made before entering the classroom and with decisions made in the midst of classroom interaction.

The three chapters reflect three aspects of teaching mathematics:

- mathematics itself and how people come to know in mathematics;
- verbal interactions with pupils about mathematics;
- design of mathematical tasks and initiation of mathematical activity.

In each case, some standard views are outlined, and some particular aspects are highlighted as worthy of attention. The aspects we have chosen to stress should be treated as frames in the sense of a picture frame which, by forming a boundary, focuses attention on detail which might otherwise not be noticed, owing to the complexity of the whole. The purpose is to stimulate reflection, not to prescribe actions.

Chapter 1
Beliefs and knowledge in mathematics

This chapter looks at the ways in which teaching a topic is influenced by teachers' ideas about the nature of mathematics and mathematical knowledge. Both the tasks that teachers choose and the particular aspects that they stress when children are engaged in activity will reflect the differing beliefs held as well as their knowledge of mathematical content and their preferred ways of presenting it in the classroom. To see what is at issue here, we start by exploring the ways in which quite different emphases can be given to a topic.

Stressing different aspects of a topic

We treat the issue of varying emphases from two perspectives: first, we look at some ways in which different aspects of a topic are emphasized in the manner a task is presented and then, second, at a divergence between the intentions of the devisers of a curriculum innovation and its implementation.

Treating a topic in different ways

When a teacher gets a class to carry out a task, there are always particular aspects that are being stressed. The teacher is often unconscious of these stressings and yet they determine the messages given to the pupils about what is important in the task and, hence, in the topic of which it forms a part.* To illustrate the differences that can occur, we first of all focus on a task which is frequently used in the upper junior or lower secondary age group: generating sequences through patterns of matchsticks, cubes, counters, tiles or whatever. A group of children are given – or devise – a method for producing a sequence of squares with matchsticks.

They are asked questions such as:

How would you make the next picture in the sequence?

How many squares will there be in the next picture, and the next?

How many matches will be needed to make the next picture, and the next?

What is the purpose of tasks like these? Why are they now regularly used in classrooms? They were almost unknown twenty years ago and the use of physical materials, the ways in which sequences were produced from shapes, and the attention given to generalizing number sequences were novel when they were first promoted. Such a task was once seen by many teachers of mathematics as out of the ordinary run of school mathematics, if not actually irrelevant to the mathematics curriculum. That it now appears to be widely acceptable indicates that individual teachers have perceptions, not only of what are suitable tasks for children but also of what is legitimate mathematical knowledge, and these perceptions change over time.

For most teachers, the source of such tasks will be a textbook, a scheme, a teacher resource book or another teacher. Examples of three treatments of shape sequences are given on the next two pages. Each is taken from a section of work on creating such sequences and so assumes some familiarity with previous questions.

Although at first sight these examples appear to be similar, they stress rather different aspects. Some of the things stressed include:

- predicting the values in the number pattern;
- finding a number pattern;
- finding a formula;
- describing how the shapes are produced;
- substituting in a formula;
- asking 'How do we find how many there are in shape 37, shape 100?';
- drawing up tables;
- organizing information in a systematic way.

Example A stresses the creation of a number pattern via a table of values and then seeks to generalize the pattern by a formula. Example B concentrates more on the building of the shapes and does not use a number pattern, neither does Example C

---

* The tasks that teachers choose and their notion of what constitutes 'a topic' are formed from their knowledge of texts, tasks and activities, as well as from their beliefs about mathematics. These other aspects are pursued in Chapter 3.

Example A

1.

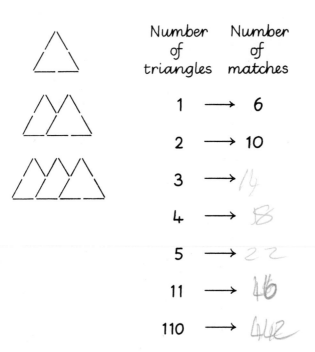

Number of triangles	Number of matches
1	→ 6
2	→ 10
3	→ *14*
4	→ *18*
5	→ *22*
11	→ *46*
110	→ *442*

2. Explain in words how to get the second number from the first. *add 4*

3. The whole mapping is given by

$$Z \longrightarrow N+4 \quad (N-1) \times 4 + 6$$

Source: DIME Pre-algebra Project, 1984, p. 10

Example B

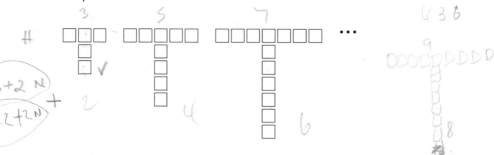

(a) Draw the next shape in the sequence.
(b) Describe the shapes succinctly, as if to someone in the room who hasn't seen them, in such a way that she will be able to duplicate the sequence.
(c) Write down a rule which will produce an ever-growing sequence with these as the first few terms.
(d) How many squares will be needed for the 10th shape, the 37th shape ...?

Adapted from Routes to/Roots of Algebra (Open University, 1985)

Example C

Here the matches make a row of hexagons.

C1 Draw two more rows with different numbers of hexagons.

C2 Let *h* stand for the number of hexagons in the row, and *m* for the number of matches.

Draw the machine chain for working out *m* when you know *h*.

$M = H \times 5 + 6$

Check that it works for the arrangements you drew.

C3 Write down the formula connecting *h* and *m*.

C4 (a) If *h* = 12, what is *m*? 66 (b) If *h* = 20, what is *m*? 106

C5 If you make a row of hexagons with 116 matches, how many hexagons will there be?

$116 = H \times 5 + 6$

$H = 52$

Source: SMP, 1983, p. 4

which emphasizes the use of a formula and substituting numbers for a variable. These textbook extracts are, of course, only a resource for teachers, who will present the task and further shape the activity in the class according to *their* perceptions of the important aspects. For the children the meaning of their activity will be determined in part by the aspects being emphasized because they will generally aim to carry out what the teacher seems to require. Their perception of the task will be different depending whether their focus of attention is on:

- making connections in the sequence of numbers;
- how the shapes are built up;
- producing different ways in which to find the number of matches in a given, but unspecified, shape.

The way in which a teacher develops a task in class will be due not only to how the teacher sees the mathematics of the situation but also to a host of other concerns: for example whether actual matchsticks are available, whether the teacher feels it important that each child does some writing or works individually. Although these are crucial contributions to the way pupil activity is conceived and develops, we concentrate on the stressings arising from teachers' mathematical frameworks.

Although we talk of 'the task', it is perhaps better to think of all tasks as potential situations which will be specified in different ways by different teachers on different occasions. The tasks themselves, and the resultant pupil activity, can become appreciably different with different teachers. This effect is even more marked when a teacher uses equipment such as geoboards or number blocks which can have a wide variety of mathematical tasks based upon them. A teacher might use such materials for different purposes at various times (indeed this is one of their attractions) so the mathematics encountered in the situation is even more in the hands of the teacher. An infant school teacher, working with an 'equalizer balance' where children hang metal rings on to hooks, might use it to:

- demonstrate comparing the sizes of two numbers;
- establish the equivalence of pairs such as 2 + 3 and 4 + 1;
- explore the links between addition and multiplication (7 + 13 = 2 × 10);
- start to look at algebraic ideas (What do we have to put on here to make it balance?);

and any of a host of other possibilities.

Even where teachers start from an apparently closely defined mathematical task, the ways in which they treat it will still draw out very different emphases. In the following instance, two teachers taught lessons using the same starting activity which was called 'Piles of Stones'.*

Two classes of third-year secondary pupils were asked to solve a set of problems similar to the following:

> There are two piles of stones. The second pile has 23 more stones than the first pile. There are 141 stones altogether. Find how many stones there are in each pile.

> There are three piles of stones. The second pile has 5 times as many stones as the first pile, and the third pile has 3 less than the first pile. There are 207 stones altogether. Find how many stones there are in each pile.

> *(Adapted from Wigley et al., 1981)*

The classes were told to solve the problems by whatever method they wished – it was expected that they would solve them informally, by trial and improvement, possibly developing systematic methods for later problems.

In the next lesson, the teachers showed the pupils an algebraic method for solving the problems, symbolizing the number of stones in one of the piles as x, writing each of the other piles in terms of x and forming an equation which they could then solve. The children were asked to do the same questions as before, but this time algebraically.

At this stage, the emphases in the two classes were quite different. One of the teachers said:

> *I now want them to learn the appropriate algebraic techniques. They have gained a feeling for the context, they already have answers and so they will be able to check their solutions to the equations.*

The other described his intentions as:

---

* We are grateful for Dave Wilson for drawing our attention to this example.

The focus is now no longer on getting the right answer but on reinterpreting what they have done. I want them to compare each step in the algebraic method with their previous method and think what the algebra means.

What the children were asked to do depended on how teachers interpreted the task in the light of their beliefs about algebra in school. The first of these teachers emphasized that the techniques were the important thing, whereas the second tried to get the pupils to engage with the meaning of the algebraic statements. Although it might seem desirable to stress both of these aims, it is often not possible. When teachers make choices of emphases they necessarily exclude other possibilities.

Encountering others' intentions

When choosing or adapting a task, teachers always put their own interpretations and agenda on to it. This process is inevitable because all teachers perceive their teaching situation in their own way; but the interpretations may or may not coincide with the intentions of the original deviser of a task. Curriculum designers produce ever-new ways in which they attempt to convey their intentions, for example, through teachers' guides and videos, in individualized schemes which bypass the teacher with workcards produced directly for the pupils, by producing software which is an essential part of the course, by tying the materials to examination questions. Attempts have been made to produce materials that are 'teacher-proof' – ones that embody the intentions of the designers in such a way that teachers cannot avoid carrying them out. Such attempts are never likely to be successful because teachers have their own priorities and they use curriculum materials to help them solve the problems of teaching and learning as they see them. However, for teachers, an outcome of using a new task will almost always be some change in their perceptions of suitable tasks and appropriate emphases to make.

But there is a problem here. Not all possible interpretations of a task are equally valid. Teachers coming to a topic they have not taught before will have to imagine the intentions of the devisers of the tasks. For newly-qualified teachers or those involved in extensive curriculum development this can be a major difficulty, although teachers may gradually be able to come to understand such intentions or may be able to use the ideas in a different, yet equally valid, way. Indeed, experienced teachers are frequently able to use their expertise to transcend their partial understanding. But if they are themselves insecure in this area, or have purposes concerning mathematics teaching that do not fit with the intentions of the designers, the teachers might then use ideas, texts, materials in such a way that the pupils engage in activities of little worth.

This happened frequently with the topic of 'number bases' in the curriculum reforms that took place during the 1960s. The originators of work on multi-base arithmetic were quite explicit about their aims: its purpose was to assist in the understanding and use of base ten, especially of place value. It was felt that by using the place-value system in bases five and eight, and through becoming aware of what they had in common with base ten, children would gain greater understanding. Because working in base five or eight had not been in the curriculum before, many teachers had no intentions of their own concerning such activities, and, abetted by textbooks, they had children working on 'sums' in these bases just as they did in their normal base ten. For the children, the emphasis became the same as the emphasis for base ten work – facility at doing arithmetic – but now in base five or eight: a skill of no practical or educational value.

It is hard to see how teachers could have done otherwise. Even when the teacher saw that the intention was to give the pupils insight into the base ten system, it was not clear how this was to be effected. The texts they used, the examinations the (secondary) pupils sat, contained 'sums' in various bases. The means of gaining insight appeared to be by computational facility.

Most children who were in schools in the 1970s worked on number bases and gained little from the experience. The topic was eventually abandoned after widespread criticism stemming, in part, from adverse comments in the HMI report *Aspects of Secondary Education* (HMI, 1979).

With hindsight, what can be recognized is that one of the assumptions held by the teachers was that the major part of mathematics is a collection of methods for solving particular types of problems. With the number-base work, the problems were seen by the teachers as 'sums' in other bases and conversion from one number base to another; the methods to be taught were facility at carrying out the techniques for doing these problems. Other purposes for these problems were not usually explored. Although 'understanding of place value' was seen as the overall aim, how this understanding manifested itself and what the children could do as a consequence of it became subordinated to learning techniques for carrying out particular problems.

Teachers' beliefs and knowledge

Whereas with number bases it seems that the teachers' large-scale beliefs about mathematics were affecting the ways in which they taught the topic, with the shape sequences the decisions concerning which aspects to emphasize seem to be much more local and may be thought of as aspects of that particular task. But why would a textbook writer or the teacher using that book choose to stress one aspect rather than another? We suggest that such choices are related to views about the topic and also to more general ideas about mathematics.

Two main influences on teachers' perceptions of the mathematics they teach can be identified: their beliefs about mathematics and their knowledge of the subject matter. These are not distinct influences, because the aspects of knowledge that they stress and consider most important are affected by their global beliefs about mathematics. Conversely, their beliefs come to be shaped by the content and methods which they habitually emphasize. Frequently, in the to and fro of a lesson, the different influences create conflicts for the teacher who has to make on-the-spot decisions about how the lesson should continue.

To indicate the ways in which these conflicts happen, we return to the example of generating sequences. We now give an account of part of a lesson for a mixed-ability class of eleven-year-olds where the teacher had started the lesson by closely following the sheet shown opposite.

You will need some wooden cubes.

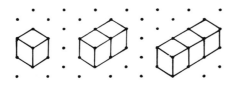

How many surfaces are there on a cube?
This number is called the cube's *surface area*.

If two cubes are stuck together, what is the surface area of the resulting solid?

If you stick three cubes together, what is the surface area?

What is the surface area of a solid of length four?
Of a solid of length five?

Make small freehand sketches like the ones above.

Copy and complete this table for the first *five* entries:

Length of solid	1	2	3	4	5	8	18	30
Surface Area	6	10						

Source: Bell, A. et al., 1978, p. 59

The pupils had blocks on their tables and had used them to count the number of faces. After some discussion which included activity with the blocks, the teacher was able to produce a table on the blackboard:

Length of solid	1	2	3	4	5	6	10	15
Surface area	6	10	14	18	22	26		

TEACHER: How many would there be for ten?

PUPIL: 42. (The teacher asks several others: all give the response 42.)

TEACHER: Has anybody got anything else?

    (He puts fifteen up on the top line.)

SUSAN: 62. (The teacher asks several others who all reply '62'.)

TEACHER: Now, how did you do it? It is 62. How did you work it out?

SUSAN: I added four.

TEACHER: You added four. Graham?

GRAHAM: I added five, and then ten, and then took off two.

TEACHER: Pardon?

GRAHAM: I added five, and then ten, and then took off two.

TEACHER: Yes. That's an interesting method, I'll have to think about that one.

Add on four each time seems to be the … anybody got another way? Anybody yet got a different way? Other than Graham's, that is …

LYNNE: (Inaudible.)

TEACHER: Ah! I don't know if any of you heard that, but Lynne timesed fifteen by four and then added two. Does that only work for that number Lynne?

LYNNE: I did it for … it works for ten.

TEACHER: You did it for the ten as well did you?

PUPIL: It works for ten.

TEACHER: It works for the others as well does it?

PUPIL: Yes, it works.

TEACHER: (Pointing at the table on the blackboard.)
What a lot of you did … in fact I think what most of you did was to look at this and saw that it went up in fours. Looked at the differences between the numbers. What Lynne did – correct me if I'm wrong, Lynne – she multiplied this by four and then added two. So, two fours are eight add two is ten; so it worked for that one. Three fours are twelve, add two is fourteen, and so on. Check it, work through all of them.

Some of the intentions behind this version of the task were explicit: the general orientation of the scheme the particular teacher was using, as well as the view of mathematics teaching held within the department, was to develop the children's 'process' abilities – to encourage them to investigate, to generalize, to devise their own methods for solving problems. One of the other objectives for this lesson, which was given in the teachers' notes, was to get pupils to generalize the number pattern by seeing the relationship between the two rows of the table (i.e. given a particular number of blocks, how can the surface area be found directly?). This was in contrast to the method of finding the surface area by noticing there was an increase of four each time a new cube was added.

The teacher is simultaneously engaged with both of these objectives. In the early exchanges, he is working with the pupils' responses which involve their own mathematical thinking; in particular, he does not comment on the correctness of their responses (even implicitly by his intonation, as the original recording shows). When he takes up Lynne's method to make it public to the class, he starts to pursue the other objective. This becomes, in the explanations that follow, a suggested method for all to try out. It is not highly emphasized, but there is a clear implication that approval is being given to the method. This contrasts with the 'adding on fours' which is acknowledged as 'what most of you did', but with the unstated implication that something different is being asked for.

The interchange with Graham illustrates a dilemma that occurs many times in a teacher's day. The teacher has the whole class waiting for his initiative; Graham says something unexpected. The teacher has to make an instant decision about whether to follow Graham's path – taking into account issues such as his feeling about its possible incorrectness and relevance, the degree of attention of the rest of the class, the importance of stressing the 'legitimate' method mentioned in the teachers' notes, the amount of time left in that lesson. He chooses not to pursue Graham's method nor to clarify what he meant. On later reflection this method turns out to be equally valid and might have formed the basis of a worthwhile class activity in the exploration of different ways of arriving at the result.

The teacher had to act, had to make a decision that implied some course of action and excluded others. The extract indicates how such decisions cannot simultaneously satisfy all of the mathematical aims of a lesson. The teacher focuses attention on a *particular strategy* for finding the formula rather than on generating methods which produce the result or on getting the pupils to generalize or on one of the other aims suggested above. This conflicts with and displaces his earlier attention to valuing pupils' contributions.

An experienced teacher has acquired a huge amount of practical knowledge about teaching in classrooms. In the practice of teaching many strands are interwoven: knowledge of oneself, of methods of teaching, of curriculum development, of the social context of teaching, of the subject matter of mathematics. The teacher's choices in the course of a lesson will frequently involve considerations of all of these, mostly not consciously. Many of the influences appear to be local – concerning the issues that the teacher wants to stress in a particular task. But, as can be seen in the example above, these are frequently reflections of the global beliefs held by a teacher.

Beliefs are 'global' in the sense that they underlie a wide range of topics; other beliefs may be much more local, concerned with, say, the important aspect of a particular topic or activity.

Beliefs about mathematics

What kinds of global beliefs might teachers hold concerning mathematics? A few of them have been mentioned. The belief that a major part of mathematics is 'techniques for solving problems' provides an instance of a large-scale framework probably shared by most teachers of mathematics. They are likely to have other such frameworks which may conflict with or support this one; for example, one that stresses 'understanding'. Teachers who see mathematics largely as a set of techniques frequently stress the importance of and pursue 'understanding' because it helps learners use and apply the methods more reliably and effectively.

Thompson (1984) in a study of how primary and secondary teachers' conceptions of mathematics affected their classroom practice, found beliefs such as:

> The primary purpose of mathematics is to serve as a tool for the sciences and other fields of human endeavor.

Mathematics is accurate, precise, and logical.

Changes in the content of mathematics occur only at the extreme as it continues to expand.

Mathematics is mysterious – its broad scope and the abstractness of some of its concepts make it impossible for a person to understand it fully.

The content of mathematics is 'cut and dried'. Mathematics offers few opportunities for creative work.

Mathematics is logical and free of emotions. Its study trains the mind to reason logically. Mathematical activity is like 'mental calisthenics'.

(Thompson, 1984, pp.110, 113, 116)

Other frequently held beliefs about the nature of mathematics are:

- a collection of techniques for solving particular kinds of problems;
- a problem-solving activity;
- an essentially useful subject, providing the means to cope with aspects of everyday life;
- a set of memorizable techniques and skills;
- a logical sequence of development;
- a subject for experimentation, proposing, checking and proving conjectures.

Individual teachers might hold a number of these beliefs. What interests us here is not so much these statements of belief but rather the ways in which certain beliefs that teachers hold influence their actions in the classroom. It is perhaps useful to contrast teaching mathematics with teaching English. English lessons are frequently seen as vehicles for dealing with children's emotions and experiences, and so the tasks a teacher gives may offer opportunities for these to arise. Because mathematics is not usually seen as a medium for these aspects of a pupil's life, certain kinds of activity often encountered in English lessons rarely occur when mathematics is being taught.

The often implicit and unstated beliefs of teachers may be rather different from their claims about what they do or are trying to do. Thompson found that there could be large discrepancies between *explicit* aims and actions. Even teachers who have well-integrated ideas and actions are unlikely to realize their aims exactly in practice, especially if these involve intrinsically difficult curriculum activities such as real problem solving or helping children become more autonomous inquirers. We should not expect, therefore, that teacher statements of their beliefs will correspond to observable stressings in class. The beliefs teachers hold are often manifest in lessons – especially critical incidents where they are making decisions – but they can also emerge by examining reactions to developments in the curriculum. We consider two such situations.

Developing arithmetic

Although calculators are being used more and more in primary schools, many primary teachers feel it to be important to continue teaching paper-and-pencil methods of calculation. To abandon traditional methods and go over to the use of calculators for all non-mental calculations is a deeply threatening act for the majority of teachers. This is not merely due to the replacement of one method by another, but because the main means of structuring the number work throughout the primary school is undermined. Most textbooks and much classroom practice progress from work with small numbers to work on larger ones and move from simple calculating methods with small numbers to more complicated means of calculating needed with larger numbers. Moreover, this progression to ever larger numbers and more complex algorithms not only structures the way number is taught, but also becomes the content of the number curriculum.

The use of calculators in the Primary Initiatives in Mathematics Education (PrIME) project forced some teachers to reconsider their thinking about this. Teachers in the project found:

- Given the freedom to explore mathematics with the calculator children do things 'out of order', because they are no longer constrained by their ability to calculate with pencil and paper.

  ...

- We can no longer speak with confidence about what children are capable of understanding. Young children use large numbers, exhibit an understanding of place value, make use of negative numbers. All these have happened through the use of a calculator without the formal teaching of the topic.

(The PrIME Project, 1991)

The PrIME project's response to these difficulties was to visualize the mathematics curriculum as 'a map made up of regions rather than being made up of bricks that build on top of one another'. The teacher will make judgements on which areas of the map a child needs further work on and will produce tasks for this purpose. This much more diffuse structure is likely to cause problems in organizing mathematics lessons. There also remain questions about what the children can do. Hitherto, arithmetic has been about learning how to perform additions, multiplications, etc.; children could demonstrate their learning by carrying out such algorithms. Now, it is much less easy to tell what children have learned because they are not required to do such definite things.

Quadratic equations

How are quadratic equations seen in the secondary curriculum? If we look at textbooks and examination papers, their main emphasis is on *solving* the equations. Solving by factorization is stressed as especially important and the techniques associated with this (converting an expression involving sums of terms to one in factors) are given much attention. The following phrases all appear in the national curriculum for England and Wales :

- factorize algebraic expressions which arise in problems;
- solve quadratic equations by using factors, the common formula or iteration as appropriate;
- know the forms of graphs of simple functions e.g. quadratic.

The key focus of the topic of 'quadratic equations' is being able to solve such equations. Although this may seem hardly worth remarking upon, it so colours the view of quadratic equations in school mathematics that it is hard to imagine any other focus being considered as plausible.

However, in the late 1980s there was a jolt to this view. Hand-held calculators appeared that would expand and factorize quadratic expressions as well as solve a quadratic equation by means of the formula. These machines could thus carry out the techniques needed to solve quadratic equations. If they could do automatically what it was formerly expected that pupils would do by thinking and using pen and paper, what should now be taught? This is almost exactly the same question that primary school teachers have been grappling with for a decade.

One response is to say simply that things should go on pretty much as before, and that calculators could be used after children have learned how to solve quadratic equations 'properly'. This is a readily understandable reaction, but it fails to confront the challenge of such technology. Increasingly, pupils will be able to use machines like these to carry out similar procedures automatically and much more accurately and rapidly than they now do.

Should the teacher simply show pupils how to use the machine? The emphasis would then be switched from being able to solve equations personally to being able to use a machine to solve them. This is rather like the change from washing by hand to using a washing machine. With the washing machine, some old skills will be no longer needed, others will still be relevant, and there will be new things to learn such as knowing whether clothing is suitable for a machine wash and the differences between the various programmes. Similarly pupils will need certain awarenesses to be able to use these algebraic calculators. For example, they will continue to need to:

- understand algebraic notation (for example the use of the letter x, as well as the meaning of $2(x + 3)$);

- recognize and know what is meant by an equation;

- know what it means to get a solution to the equation;

- know that algebraic expressions can be transformed into equivalent versions.

The emphasis is still on *solving* the equations, however. Are there other ways of thinking about the mathematical content of quadratic equations in school?

One possibility is to examine the relationships between quadratic equations, quadratic functions and their graphs to see when (real) roots occur, how this connects to the graph, how to deduce the roots from the graph and to relate these to certain forms of the equation.

Another possibility is to explore the generation of equivalence classes of quadratic equations. It was a major historical achievement in mathematics to see $x^2 = 6 - 5x$ as the same sort of equation as $x^2 + 5x = 6$ and to be able to lump these together with many others. There are algebraic transformations that enable us to see the two equations above as 'the same', and so create the equivalence class hiding behind the phrase 'this quadratic equation'. Exploring these transformations and becoming aware of the class of equivalent expressions of one equation and of the infinite class of all quadratic equations could be the new focus of the topic.

For most of us, these changes create difficulties. We often have problems in readjusting to changes in our local beliefs about what is important in a topic, but even more so with global beliefs about the nature of things to be learned in mathematics. We are moved to ask what the pupils can *do* as a result of learning this. This shows how deeply embedded is our notion that mathematics consists of techniques for solving problems. Such an orientation also explains some of the difficulties of curriculum innovations that do not have techniques and methods as their focus. This issue is one which arises particularly with the advent of the 'new technology', whether it be calculators in the primary school or graph plotters in the upper secondary.

Ways of knowing mathematics

From beliefs on the nature of mathematics, we turn to the forms mathematical knowledge takes. When we say that we *know* some mathematics, what kind of thing is it we know? This might seem to be a rather rarefied, philosophical, issue but teachers' practice is guided by beliefs concerning the nature of mathematical knowledge. When teachers give out practical equipment, or get children to do an exercise, or ask them to visualize a shape, they are implementing their beliefs about what counts as legitimate mathematical knowledge and about the forms in which this exists.

On being asked what a mathematics lesson is about, replies such as addition, graphs, area, measurement or whatever is the general mathematical topic area might be given. These might be amplified to, say, a particular method of adding two-digit numbers, or drawing graphs of straight lines from their formulae. Further probing reveals that associated with any such aspect of content are forms in which the mathematical knowledge is embedded. It is not just that the teacher wants a pupil to know what 'cosine' is, but also to associate it with some rule ('adjacent over hypotenuse'), or some image ('a point moving round a circle'), or a mnemonic ('SOHCAHTOA'). Young children working with number will be expected have their knowledge embedded in words and symbols, diagrammatic representations, images – visual and tactile – of physical materials, and probably many others. Teachers will stress different ways of knowing for different pupils, but will tend to concentrate on one or two particular forms in a particular topic. It is often thought that pupils get confused when they are asked to work on knowledge embedded in several different forms. Again, teachers will differ in what they consider the most appropriate forms of knowledge for a particular aspect of content.

It is important to realize that the forms of knowledge a teacher attends to are not inherent in the mathematical topic but are constructions, usually by mathematical educators, acquired by the teacher from their own experience of being a learner as well as from books, colleagues and tutors. Even then the process is not complete for all teachers constantly adapt their original notions in the day-to-day life of the classroom, stressing different aspects that seem necessary for the pupils' learning. As Elbaz (1983) says 'the teacher's subject matter knowledge, no less than other areas of her knowledge, is practical knowledge, shaped by and for the practical situation' (p. 55).

Although teachers may start with conceptions of the 'proper' form of knowledge appropriate to a topic, their view is likely to be tempered by what appears to work successfully in the classroom. Teachers are constantly mediating between their academic allegiances to mathematics – even when they do not see themselves primarily as teachers of mathematics – and the need to engage pupils. Their beliefs concerning appropriate kinds of mathematical knowledge will be forged from these experiences.

In getting children to work on number sequences or multiplication, teachers will select and emphasize certain aspects of knowledge that they feel important for the children to have. Such knowledge will include not just images or rules but particular forms of them. For each mathematical topic they regularly teach, a teacher has ideas about 'the most useful forms of representation of those ideas, the most powerful analogies, illustrations, examples, explanations and demonstrations – in a word, the ways of representing and formulating the subject that make it comprehensible to others' (Shulman, 1986, p. 9). We now look at two topic areas to see the ways in which this process happens.

Negative numbers

In the teaching of negative numbers, much effort is given to creating and using embodiments of such numbers – stories about number-lines, cheques and bills on accounts, temperature scales, situations involving filling and emptying or rising and falling, speeds in different directions, movement on grids. Such devices are not merely intended to make it easier to learn about negative numbers, but are also attempts to give children particular kinds of knowledge about negative numbers.*

This knowledge will be in the form of images that can be referred to, stories to resort to in order to interpret the symbols, experiences designed to give children 'an intuitive feel' for how negative numbers work and some contexts in which these numbers can be used. In addition to these aspects, teachers might also want children to have formalized rules to deal with, say 2 – (–3). Some such rules for subtracting a negative number are:

> minus minus makes plus;
>
> subtracting a negative number is the same as adding a positive;
>
> $x - (- y) = x + y.$

---

* Even to speak of *negative* numbers is another such device – in the past, these have been called 'minus numbers'. Before the 1960s it was unusual to speak of *positive and negative numbers*. Other writers have used 'signed numbers' or 'directed numbers'. Along with new names various symbolisms have been invented – Richard Skemp used L3, R4; SMP followed the American Madison Project with $^+3$, $^-4$. Others have used colour coding.

Even these rules appeal to different forms of knowledge. Although the first seems a purely symbolic knowing, it also uses rhythmic language; the second makes an appeal to a meaning of the symbols in terms of addition and subtraction; the last is an algebraic expression in which children have to know that x and y can be replaced by (unsigned) numbers. Each of these has to be meaningful to be useful and it is well known that children make mistakes in applying them.

Subtraction

Teachers want children to have an intuitive feel for subtraction as 'taking away', as 'losing something'. They also want children to understand the relationship to addition, to verbal forms such as 'seven minus four equals three' and to symbolic forms such as $7 - 4 = 3$, to have a sense of the kinds of problems that can be solved by using subtraction. Later, children need to be able to use one of the standard subtraction algorithms and to carry out mental subtractions. Each of these will be presented in distinctive fashion: with physical objects to count or with a worksheet of exercises or verbally. Teachers are likely to want children to be able to move between these different aspects and will provide tasks to help in encouraging this.

Teachers will make numerous decisions – to count many different kinds of objects or only a few kinds, to use words like 'take away', 'lose', either initially or when dealing with sums on paper; to relate objects and 'sums' to a number-line, how often to use a number-line. They will decide how to present the subtraction algorithm: whether to tie it to apparatus such as Dienes blocks or bundles of matches, or offer some routines based on the vertical layout (each with their associated language: 'putting on the doorstep', 'borrowing', 'changing the one to a ten'). If all goes well and the children learn how to subtract competently and efficiently, teachers will be satisfied with their methods (although if a child has difficulties, it is likely that more attention will be given to the child's thinking and the methods used).

As time goes on, teachers choose tasks for children in order to reinforce what they consider to be the most important aspects of subtraction; for one teacher this may be facility with the algorithm, for another the link with addition, for a third the connection with intuition, for yet another the relationship to a physical representation. Of course the same teacher may emphasize each of these aspects at different times (although typically as facility improves, some aspects recede into the background).

Each of these aspects offers only a partial view of subtraction and very often the teacher only has time to deal with some of these before passing a child on to another teacher. Such partial views may be adequate for the child's current needs – their limitations may not be apparent at that time but will emerge later. Thus, it is likely to be only when the child meets negative numbers in the secondary school that the intuitive sense that 'subtraction makes numbers smaller' will create a conflict.

In the best cases, the child might have a well-rounded knowledge of subtraction, but more likely there will be some forms clearer than others: there will be images, rules, word associations, intuitions concerning when subtraction is appropriate. Not all of these will have been explicitly taught – the children will have made their own connections between some of the forms and these may reinforce or conflict with the teacher's intentions.

The forms of mathematical knowledge such as those for subtraction and negative numbers often seem specific to a particular topic and experienced teachers draw upon a repertoire of such examples and embodiments. The ones they choose will depend on what they have found most effective over years of teaching or on which aspects they wish to stress. However, such choices will finally rest on their beliefs concerning the most desirable forms for mathematical knowledge.

In the study by Thompson (1984), different teachers said that they tried to:

- get their pupils to identify the appropriate operation for solving an arithmetic problem by focusing on key words;
- appeal to the pupils' intuitions to make the material meaningful;
- get pupils to see the relationship between a new topic and those already studied.

Every time teachers choose a task they will stress their beliefs about the desirability of thinking with an image, or of being able to use symbolic rules, or of the need for strong intuitions, or whatever. We now attempt to elucidate these various forms of knowledge in mathematics.

Forms of knowledge in mathematics

The Cockcroft Report (DES, 1982) offered six forms of mathematical knowledge: facts, skills, conceptual structures, general strategies for problem solving, appreciation of the nature of mathematics, attitudes towards mathematics. This list has been widely quoted but its categories are very general, and not easily applicable to classroom practice. For example, 'facts' might occur in many forms – as symbols, as a word string, as images. Moreover, the classification takes no account of aspects such as intuitions or stories (as the 'debits' and 'credits' for dealing with signed numbers).

Each of us knows about subtraction in our own way: we will call up personal examples, forms, stories, patterns of words, rituals, images when we recognize a situation that involves 'subtraction'. Knowledge about subtraction does not exist as a thing out there that can be acquired by learners (although most of the time teachers – and the rest of us – act as if it does). Such knowledge is constructed by the learner and what form it takes depends on the contexts met, the learners' perception of the tasks they have been given by teachers and a host of other aspects. It is impossible to separate the knowledge from the way the learner acquires it: to learn something in a different way is to learn something different.

When we answer the question 'How do you know that?' we justify things or show others by appealing to the forms that we know – whether an image, an intuition or symbolic form. We have mentioned a number of these forms in discussing the previous examples: here we draw them together and look at some others. The forms of knowledge that we shall discuss are language, symbols, imagery, contexts, techniques and methods, perceptions, intuitions, practical knowledge, and experience. Before we discuss these in more detail, it is worth noticing that they do not occur in easily separable compartments. An image might include language or an intuition might be formed by experience and action.

Language

Some of our knowledge will be embodied in the language we use to talk and think about it. This includes the words and phrases used in everyday speech as well as the technical vocabulary found in schemes and textbooks. The words that trigger the use of subtraction – those like 'how many more?', 'the difference between' or technical ones like 'borrowing and paying back' (but which draw upon everyday images) fall into both categories of language. They make reference to informal knowledge and to specific procedures taught in school. Language knowledge includes rules and precepts (BODMAS and 'minus minus makes plus') as well as verbal formulae ('then bring down the next digit', 'multiply the bottoms and the tops'). The stories that are told or the contexts that are described with negative numbers make use of their language as well as their power to evoke images: debits and credits, left and right.

Children are repeatedly asked to listen to, to read, to write and to talk about the ideas that they are learning; the words and phrases used are adopted (and adapted) by them and in some sense the ideas *are* the language used.

Symbols

Very often mathematical knowledge exists as symbols.* The numerals 37 or 142, the equation $y = 2x - 5$ can function partly as images to help call up other associations, but they are also operated with as symbols. Symbols can be seen as 'symbolic forms' in which, for example, the 'x' in $2x - 5$ can be replaced by 3 or even $6a^2$. In performing the subtraction sum

$$\begin{array}{r} 142 \\ - 37 \\ \hline \end{array}$$

it is common to work with the symbols as if they were objects. The symbols are said to 'take on a life of their own'. The images and language associated with the symbols recede and we frequently operate purely with symbols, moving from one set of symbols to another. The steps of the subtraction sum are evoked by the symbols: we do not think about the sizes of the numbers, or the contexts from which they are drawn while we are performing the calculation. Similarly, when solving a quadratic equation, we can carry out formal algebraic steps without interpreting them in terms of the graph of the function or the problem from which the equation arose. Walkerdine (1988) gives a telling account of how, with young children learning place value, symbols are being used in such a way even when it would appear that the children are recording the results of practical experiences. A teacher is aiming to develop a sense of place value by working with bundles of matchsticks where, for example, 23 matches are made into two bundles of ten and a collection of three.

---

* Symbols and their connection to language are discussed much more fully in the companion volume, *Mathematics: Symbols and Meanings*.

> The teacher's intention in giving the children matchsticks to count and group – and represent with the numerals in a place-value system – is that the relations of value between the numerals in that system will be apparent to the children because they will be presented concretely as relations between bundles and single matchsticks.
>
> *(Walkerdine, 1988, p. 169)*

Through her detailed analysis of the interchanges between teacher and children, Walkerdine is able to show that:

> On the contrary, it is the properties of the place-value systems which are used to make the matchsticks, and the grouping of them into bundles of ten, which signify in particular ways. If the teacher did not [start with the symbols] there would be no reason for the children to give the groupings of matchsticks any significance. …
>
> The children's activity does not provide the experience from which they may abstract that understanding. In fact, the properties of the place-value system are used to help the children to understand their activity.
>
> *(Walkerdine, 1988, pp. 169, 170)*

Imagery

Images include not only visual ones of various degrees of vividness, but also physical awareness derived from muscular responses when using equipment (including the body), or strong aural associations, and so on. Imagery is individual: one person's mental image of (or feeling for) something will be different from someone else's, and have different associations. A pupil will call up an image of a teacher cupping his hands to indicate the need for brackets; another will associate a particular inflection with counting backwards. Other pupils who were present when these images were formed may not have anything comparable.

Imagery is generally associated with geometry – but is also inescapably present when working with number. The numbers may arise from physical images or situations (as in the sequences of squares or cubes earlier), but perhaps more importantly, there are also images for holding particular ways of evoking numbers. These include the layout of a subtraction sum on the page, a number-line, a hundreds table, an image of Unifix cubes, the tabular display of a sequence, number spirals, and arrow diagrams. There are also images to help hold a sense of operations: thus, multiplication can be imagined as a square – or by sheets of spotty paper. Diagrams such as:

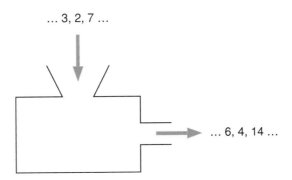

are intended to help children gain a sense of an operation as a whole.

In each of these children take over the image and use it to help them work with the operation. Because imagery is not necessarily visual it could include rhythmic counting or a physical sense of closeness of say, the *ab* in *ab* + *c*.

Images of aspects of mathematics are often called up without premeditation and so are not readily inspected by many teachers. Indeed:

> ... part of the difficulty that many people have with arithmetic (or algebra) is that they have not realised that they need to work on some internalised mental image other than that of the marks on paper which record particular numbers and operations. This is why it is useful and important to offer students 'representative' images such as wooden rods or rhythmic counting, number-lines or number-squares.

> *(Tahta, 1985, p. 5)*

Much of the work in early algebra in recent years has involved attempts to offer children mental images for algebraic thinking – some examples are number machines, arrow diagrams, or a box instead of a letter for a variable.

Contexts

Here we are referring to knowing the sorts of situations where a topic arises and the types of questions which can be dealt with by that topic. These may be everyday contexts in which the idea of subtraction can be seen to be relevant or specifically mathematical ones. Most mathematical topics become identified as such because they represent an approach that has been developed for dealing with a range of questions or problems and these problems often occur in particular contexts. There is often a complicated relationship between the contexts and the mathematics associated with them. Thus, directed numbers occur in a fairly straightforward way in an everyday context such as temperatures, but they are rather more hidden in bank credits and debits, and still more so in, say, movements up and down 'Top Twenty' charts or Football League tables. Although all of these contexts are in some sense *about* directed numbers, the language and symbolism associated with each context is so particular that it disguises the relationship and makes it difficult to see in terms of the topic of directed numbers.

Techniques and methods

When looking at certain topics in mathematics, the same sorts of techniques are encountered over and over again. The ideas of splitting a number into parts, of taking the complement in ten, are techniques that will be required in many of the situations where subtraction appears. Being able to transform an equation into an equivalent form or factorize an expression given as sums of terms are techniques useful for solving equations.

Such techniques and methods are often called 'skills', and much of the writing on skills, and the assumptions about what skills are needed in arithmetic, say, implies that there are routines that can be memorized and carried out automatically. This seems to be a form of reification: we see skilful performance and deduce that the individual possesses some attributes called 'skills'. This is to oversimplify greatly. Accomplished performance requires:

- recognizing contexts and perceiving which are the key features;
- having a variety of responses to what you see needs to be done, and being able to choose between them;
- carrying out the necessary actions to realize your choice.

(*Adapted from Welford, 1987, pp. 715–6*)

The term 'skills' is usually taken to refer only to the last of these, but not only are the three aspects interdependent (in the sense that the discriminations required for recognizing and choosing help in carrying out the actions) but they are developed together.

Perceptions

These are the most direct forms of knowing: seeing that there are more beads on this necklace than on that; that this shape is square and that shape round; that there is a diagram for each arrangement of matches. Each time children can say 'I can see it', they are using perception. Its characteristic is that it is immediate. Modern views on the nature of perception are that there is no such thing as 'just seeing', but that our existing knowledge and assumptions actively affect what we perceive. Children learn to perceive what is being stressed as important in particular contexts: they learn to perceive differently in different lessons. In looking at a collection of beads, they notice different things in a mathematics lesson than in an art lesson. Similarly, people's perceptions develop with their knowledge – initially, a child may see a geometric figure as a whole: it is only later that the triangles can be seen 'in it'. Perceptions can become quite extraordinary. In an account of twins, aged 26, who had been diagnosed as autistic and had lived in an institution since they were seven, Sacks recounts:

> A box of matches on their table fell, and discharged its contents on the floor: '111,' they both cried simultaneously; and then, in a murmur, John said '37'. Michael repeated this, John said it a third time and stopped. I counted the matches – it took me some time – and there were 111.

'How could you count the matches so quickly?' I asked. 'We didn't count,' they said. 'We *saw* the 111.'

(Sacks, 1986, p. 189)

Intuitions

These may be closely linked with images or language, but they are what we refer to when we describe having a feeling that something is the case when we do not necessarily have evidence for it. An intuition involves no conscious processes of explicit thinking or reasoning and yet is not a perception. It can be described as a supposition which views something as self evident and yet it exceeds the observable. By operating on an embodiment of directed numbers, it is possible to gain an intuitive feel for the way two numbers cancel or reinforce each other; by playing games which involve choosing numbers, it is possible to develop an intuitive feeling for the relative sizes of numbers. Intuitions are necessary to function mathematically and yet hold particular dangers: they are often only partially true for a limited range of aspects. Early intuitions, while essential, may become deeply ingrained and create difficulties in moving on. An example is the intuition that multiplication makes bigger which is an important attribute of early development of a sense of multiplication (both for the relative sizes of numbers and understanding, say, the everyday use such as 'the rabbits were multiplying fast') but which is often not modified and so causes trouble when children deal with numbers less than one or with negative numbers.

Practical knowledge

This is knowledge as action: from our earliest days we learn by handling, sucking, squeezing, pushing. The knowledge acquired in this way is inseparable from action:

> ... in early childhood ... we test everything to become familiar with the attributes of hardness, softness, smoothness, slipperiness, roughness, resistance to effort, to tearing, to pulling, to pushing, to fitting, etc.
>
> *(Gattegno, 1987, p. 59)*

But we start to reflect on these aspects, so that we do not need actually to carry out the actions – in new situations we have a sense of such properties without needing to perform the actions. Such knowledge might seem to be only applicable to the very earliest learning and then only to the properties of physical objects and not to mental, mathematical objects. Although this knowledge is most developed when we are young it forms the basis of knowing whether, for example, a parallelogram will fit into a frame without turning it over.

Experience

We know what it is like to be a student, a parent, a teacher, a hill-walker, an immigrant by our own experiences. Such experiences give us knowledge unobtainable in any other way and include:

> ... the sense in which I know what it is to be poor, to fight for a cause, to belong to a nation, to join or abandon a church or a party, to feel nostalgia, terror, the omnipresence of a god, to understand a gesture, a work of art, a joke, a man's character, that one is transformed or lying to oneself.

> *(Berlin, 1981, p. 116)*

But, as with practical knowledge, we only learn some of these through our own personal experiences. The less direct ways of coming to know such things are when

> ... the experience of others is sufficiently woven into one's own to be seized quasi-directly, as a part of constant intimate communication; and ... by the working (sometimes by a conscious effort) of the imagination.

> *(Berlin, 1981, p. 116)*

At a less profound level, we can become acquainted with a field of study, with algebra or trigonometry.

> Acquaintance is a way of knowing used by all of us when we are conscious that familiarity is contributing something definite to what is experienced as familiar. ...

> The acquaintance with their field is what makes scientists more than analytic instruments. It makes them know what is relevant, what is important, what is significant and needs their attention.

> *(Gattegno, 1987, pp. 69, 70)*

This is perhaps what the Cambridge mathematician G. H. Hardy meant when he said of the brilliant, self-taught number-theorist, Ramanujan, 'the integers were his friends'.

Summary

Teachers have knowledge about ways of teaching mathematical content which arises from their experience as both teacher and learner, and from texts, INSET courses and colleagues. They embody this in their actions in the classroom – in the choices they make about approaches to a topic which emphasize some aspects over others. Since different teachers have different emphases, on what basis do teachers make these choices? This chapter has tried to suggest that the choices are highly dependent on teachers' beliefs about the nature of mathematical knowledge and on their global beliefs concerning mathematics. These beliefs reveal themselves in preferences for particular forms of content knowledge ('what is really important is ...'). Such preferences are unlikely to be random, favouring one form of knowledge in this topic and a different one in another. Although mostly implicit and unexamined they can be revealed, at least in part, by examining one's teaching and one's attitude to curriculum changes. Bringing these preferences out into the open is likely to help teachers become aware of the forms they are at present ignoring and help them make more informed choices.

Chapter 2
Frames for teaching

Introduction

Every act by a teacher in a mathematics classroom is a manifestation not only of their perception of mathematics but also of their perception of what is involved in teaching (and by implication also in learning) mathematics. How a teacher behaves in the classroom in a mathematical situation, and the habitual interactions which take place, speak volumes to pupils about mathematics and about the possibilities in it for them.*

Everyone has ideals and aims and everyone has ways of dealing with standard situations. Unfortunately, those 'ways of dealing with' are not always consonant with the ideals. For example, it is possible to have the ideal that pupils become autonomous learners while at the same time firmly controlling all their activities. Sometimes the specific acts of teaching conflict with, or detract from, the teacher's global aims and intentions and at other times they contribute to and support them.

The totality of pupil–teacher interactions is a vast and complex domain. This chapter concentrates on just a few aspects of verbal interactions. It looks at three

---

* In a MORI poll conducted in October 1990, 57 per cent of 18- to 34-year-olds considered teachers to be 'very important' in influencing the attitudes of young people, and 90 per cent thought teachers the most influential group, ahead of MPs, trade union leaders, senior managers and religious leaders.

modes of verbal interaction, suggesting frames for probing behind some of the prevalent slogans about telling, about asking and about mathematical discussion. The final section returns to the question of beliefs and assumptions in relation to the frames presented. Since many, if not all, interactions with pupils are intended to extend pupils' thinking, and thus depend on pupils being ready for the ideas, this chapter is followed by an interlude on the notion of 'readiness' in mathematics.

Beliefs and assumptions

We begin by presenting some common perceptions of how teachers and pupils interact mathematically. Prospective mathematics teachers, when asked at interview why they want to teach mathematics, often say things like:

> *I want to enter mathematics teaching because I enjoy explaining mathematical ideas and feel I am good at it.*

The urge to tell, to make things clear for others, is strong. Practising teachers, when asked by researchers about the principles and beliefs guiding their practice in mathematics, give a range of replies, such as:

> *You've got to keep them busy.*

> *Asking pupils questions gets them to think.*

> *Pupils need lots of opportunity to practice techniques, otherwise they forget.*

> *Pupils learn best by doing things.*

> *I always try to answer a question with a question.*

> *I never tell pupils anything that they can find out for themselves.*

> *'We need to question pupils constantly and tell them nothing' (Smith, 1988, p. 47).*

> *You should never ask pupils a question which has only a single correct answer.*

When researchers subsequently observe lessons, they often find a significant discrepancy between what teachers tell them, and what they see. There are, of course, many reasons for such a discrepancy:

> ... a man's reach should exceed his grasp,
> Or what's a heaven for?

as Robert Browning suggested in his poem *Andrea del Sarto*. If there were no gap between practice and intention, there would be no room for growth. But it is also possible to be deceived. It is possible to believe in being open and non-directive and yet be seen as exerting firm direction and leaving little actual opportunity to pupils. For example, Derek Edwards and Neil Mercer (1987) concluded from analysis of videotapes and transcripts that apparently open-ended and non-directive teaching was in fact highly directive. It is possible to believe in keeping a tight rein on activities and yet be seen as a responsive and non-directive teacher.

Statements such as those given above suggest a collection of beliefs and principles, from the detailed to the general, which frame classroom practice and through which all other suggestions about teaching and learning are likely to be viewed. Striking and quotable statements may only reflect the intensity of one person's concerns at the moment they are uttered but they may also act as rules and precepts which influence and affect teaching behaviour.

In order to probe beneath scattered beliefs and principles it is essential to look in much finer detail at the interactions between teacher and pupils and among pupils. We do not attempt a full taxonomy of all ways in which teachers and pupils interact verbally as such an analysis is more likely to be overwhelming than useful. Rather than assert some *shoulds* and *oughts* we offer some distinctions between different approaches to telling, to asking, and to discussing, which might be helpful for preparing for, and being in, mathematics classrooms. The aim is to focus attention on some distinctions which may make it possible to notice opportunities in the midst of a lesson and to decide to respond freshly. Rather than analysing what others have said and done in classrooms, we want to draw attention to what it feels like to be in the midst of a classroom, not as an observer but as a participant.

Most verbal interactions involve people asking and telling. In the midst of asking and telling, it is hard not to assume that the audience is experiencing the same thoughts as the speaker. Yet asking people questions and telling them things are problematic enterprises at the best of times, whether in the classroom or outside it:*

- in asking questions, it is tempting to assume that the responder has taken the question to heart and that the reply represents what the responder thinks;

- in telling people things, it is tempting to assume that they then know what they have been told.

But just because it is easy to make inappropriate assumptions, it does not follow that asking or telling people is necessarily ineffective. When people are able to hear what is said, telling can be very helpful – just as when a seed is sown in prepared ground. When people are engaged and interested, asking can indeed be stimulating – just as when a seed germinates and begins again the cycle of growth.

Despite the simplification necessary in order to think about asking and telling, it is important to bear in mind the complexity of classroom utterances. For example, things may be said in order to control different aspects of a lesson:

- perhaps to re-focus attention, after what to the teacher is a diversion, as in 'So why do we use brackets?';

- perhaps to control the behaviour of an individual, as in 'What did I just say, Shona?';

- perhaps to signal the level of discussion intended, as in the difference between 'How wide is this desk?' and 'How can we find out how wide this desk is?' or between 'What is the name of a shape with three edges?' and 'What names shall we give to the shapes that we've found?'.

For further examples of questions which serve to control, see Ainley (1987).

---

* 'You can tell people and tell people and tell people but if they're not ready to hear you, then there's no point' – from the film *Passage to India*.

Sometimes a question hides an assertion, as in:

> *'What have you done?' meaning 'You have done something wrong';*

and an assertion is sometimes actually a question, as in:

> *'You know something else' meaning 'There is something you are overlooking that I can see. What else do you know?'*

There is also what Ainley calls the 'hovering' question, as in:

> *'This four-sided shape is called a ...' or 'This ruler is for measuring in ...'*

in which pupils are expected to fill in the missing word or words.

Thus, teacher intentions when speaking may be multiple. What is said can arise from local, detailed concern about the mathematical ideas, from larger concerns about the conduct of the lesson, and from global concerns about the nature of education and the discipline of mathematics.

Care is needed in reading and interpreting other people's beliefs through observing their classroom and even more through mere quotations and transcripts. Tone and emphasis, posture, timing and silence are notoriously difficult to transcribe and take account of, even when using videotape. Even as a participant, interpreting beliefs from behaviour is an uncertain, though frequent, enterprise. Pupils may read control into teacher questions which are not intended to be controlling and, conversely, they may not notice or remark upon a degree of control which enables lessons to proceed smoothly and efficiently. People may read into behaviour beliefs and assumptions which are 'not there' for the teacher; they may also detect beliefs of which the teacher is oblivious. In addition to aspects of control, there is, of course, the influence of the teacher's (and the pupils') perceptions of mathematics and expectations about how teaching and learning take place. Thus, pupils may read into a teacher's behaviour a description of what mathematics is about, or how it is to be pursued, even though the teacher may be unaware of what is being read and may have entirely contrary beliefs. If actions speak louder than words, it is important to be aware of one's actions and not just one's words.

Since the first person to speak after silence has fallen is usually the teacher, teaching usually begins with the teacher and so the next three sections start from teacher-talk and look at ways of interacting which involve the teacher *telling* pupils things, then at ways in which teachers try to initiate pupils' participation, through *asking questions*, and then at pupils *discussing* among themselves and interacting with a teacher who intervenes in order to help or stimulate the activity.

Telling

> If you scale a shape by a factor of k, then the perimeter is scaled by a factor of k, and the area is scaled by a factor of k^2.

This statement could be part of a formal lecture, it could signal a conjecture to be investigated over a period of time whether as a pupil's suggestion or as the teacher's repetition of a pupil's conjecture or as a suggestion from the teacher or it could be a summary of findings at the end of a period of study. In other words, utterances by themselves are simply utterances. Their effect depends on context and expectations.

As a mode of interacting with pupils, *telling* received a particularly bad press in the 1980s. Emphasis on investigation, group work and pupil experience led to a dislike of and reaction against exposition, probably as a reaction against memories of sitting in lessons being told things endlessly by a succession of teachers. But there are many circumstances in which it is not only proper and effective, but essential to tell people things.

People can be told things in more than one way. Indeed, Ainley (1987) suggests that not only assertions but also questions do their share of telling people things: things about the speaker's interests and concerns and things about how the subsequent lesson is likely to develop. People tell each other things all the time, often very effectively, though very often the significant communication is not the literal meaning of the words, but the exchange of attention – what Eric Berne (1966) called 'stroking'.* Examples of stroking include the ritualized exchanges such as 'Good morning', 'How are you?' and 'Thank you' which serve to lubricate the cogs of personal interactions. Absence of such stroking exchanges makes other 'more important' communication difficult.

There are social settings in which telling is a response to an implicit or explicit request:

> To find out the bus or train times or when a TV programme is going to be broadcast: information is wanted, not a series of questions or deflections.

> To find out how to use some new device: an invitation to 'explore for yourself' as the sole contents of the instruction booklet could be dangerous as well as unhelpful.

> To find out what someone else thinks about a topic: having them ask a series of questions is not what is wanted.

> To hear what someone has to say: going to a meeting to be put into small groups for the whole session to discuss what participants think is not what is wanted. Choosing to attend a lecture or read a book suggest an implicit wish to be told.

In school contexts, where the teacher is expected to help the pupil to learn, it is not so clear whether telling or not telling is likely to be more effective. In the midst of a complicated calculation when the answer to 'seven eights' is needed, but momentarily forgotten, the answer is what is wanted, not an invitation to work it out. But is that the most fruitful thing to do for the pupil? There are of course no rules. Any principles, such as

> *Never tell them something they can work out for themselves.*

or

> *Treat them as adults. If they ask a direct question, give them the answer.*

over-stress one aspect at the expense of another.

* Eric Berne develops this idea extensively in his old but still insightful work *Games People Play: the psychology of human relationships.*

A common feature of social situations in which telling is desirable is that someone wants to know something. Unfortunately this is not always the situation in classrooms. Pupils do not always want to know things. Sometimes they just want to cope. They want to get by. However, it may be possible to stimulate interest, to engage pupils in activity, to generate surprise or contradiction, so that the wish to know begins to form and pupils begin to take some of the initiative.

The Cockcroft report (DES, 1982) suggested a need for balance among exposition and other forms of interaction in classrooms but, for a long time afterwards, HMI continued to report that it was difficult to find a classroom in which exposition did not play a major part. Emphasis was therefore placed by the mathematics education community on small-group and individualized work. Continued emphasis on mixed-ability teaching in secondary schools reinforced interest in individualized learning schemes and so resulted in even less emphasis on exposition. There grew up in mathematics education circles a suggestion that exposition was to be avoided, that pupils should instead be given every opportunity to explore, construct and make sense for themselves. For some reason, the idea of pupils making sense for themselves is often seen as incompatible with telling them things. We shall argue that they are in fact entirely compatible. The point about telling people things is to choose carefully what to tell and when to tell it.

It is natural to want to tell people things and natural to want to be told things as well. Since it is impossible in one lifetime to discover everything for yourself, people try to learn from others. There are two awkwardnesses about 'telling'. One is choosing to tell people things that they are just about to find out for themselves anyway and so disrupting productive thought or deflating them by taking away the pleasure of discovery. The other is assuming that the hearers know what they have been told.

There is plenty of evidence that this latter, inappropriate, assumption is a common state of affairs between teachers and pupils:

> *If I've told you once, I've told you a hundred times!*

> *You were told that last (week, month, term, year, ...)*

Pupils collude in this assumption, for they often say, or behave as if they believe:

> *Just tell me once more and then I'll understand.*

If it is not sensible to assume that people know what they have been told, why tell them at all? Yet denying telling is just as unbalanced as relying upon it for the main form of interaction with pupils. To refuse to tell on the grounds that it does not help (because 'they still don't know') contradicts the belief that telling is liable to deflate or disrupt. If telling is indeed so ineffective, then it would not be possible to disrupt or deflate by telling!

Learning is a much more complex process than a simple cause and effect relationship between what the teacher says and what the pupils learn. It makes sense to tell people things when they are in a state to be able to hear, to relate to, to make connections with, and to assimilate what is being said and yet not able to work it out quickly for themselves. If people are not in a state to hear what is being said, then they are unlikely to make much of it. For example, the pupil who remarked to his mother:

> *Mr P. is being very silly at the moment. He's doing all sorts of complicated things to add fractions together, when all he needs to do is add the tops and add the bottoms.*

may not be in a position to hear the teacher's algorithm. Neither is the pupil who is confident about using a ruler, but always starts from the '1' mark *'because you always start counting from one'*.

For telling to be successful, there usually has to be something problematic, something uncertain, paradoxical or striking in order for the ground to be adequately prepared. Interest has to be aroused and awareness sharpened in order for someone to be in a position to be told something effectively. What is said has then to relate to pupils' experience and to call upon their confidence in order to push at the boundaries of their current understanding.

Three forms of telling

The following classification of forms of telling into *expounding*, *explaining* and *conjecturing* is intended to be sufficiently compact not to be unwieldy yet sufficiently discerning in order to inform practice.

Expounding

> We use the terms *expounding* and *exposition* to refer to speaking from one's own vivid images, from being in contact with mathematical ideas, like a tour guide pointing out sights of interest on either side, and providing insightful observations.

Exposition typically introduces new words or terms, new ways of thinking, new ideas. When a teacher is expounding effectively, she is exposing, or 'putting out in plain view', thoughts and ideas which have been worked on and clarified over a period of time. She is laying out the territory, indicating that a map exists, even though pupils are not expected to 'take it all in'. Aspects of a heritage of intellectual development are presented for consideration. She enters her rich world of experience and speaks vividly from there. The audience (literally, the 'hearers') are drawn into that world, as with a good story-teller.

Exposition involves pupils being in the presence of someone working and thinking mathematically, someone who is in touch with important mathematical ideas. An expositor can make the ordinary seem strange and exciting and can stimulate interest to know more or to resolve some unexpected uncertainty or surprise. Pupils do not learn how to do something from exposition, how to perform some technique just from being told or shown, but they can be inspired, stimulated and challenged. They can see that there is something surprising to be accounted for or sorted out, something unexpected to accommodate to their current intuitions.

Exposition can be a precursor to exploration. The exposition provides a vague sense or overview, a map of the territory and pupils can find out from particular examples what a certain technique or idea is about in detail. The teacher may feel, as do authors of texts and schemes, that it is necessary to demonstrate to pupils how a particular technique is carried out. But that demonstration is merely a starting point for the pupils to reconstruct and assimilate for themselves.

For example, having collected together a mass of data on height, and wrist, hand, arm and foot lengths, pupils may want to know whether one measurement can be predicted from another. A plot of wrist size against arm length (for example) is a standard technique in such circumstances, but pupils are unlikely to think of it without considerable prior experience. Telling pupils about such a technique may be helpful, including demonstrating its use (preferably using a computer program), but pupils then have to get down and use the program themselves, make their plots and contemplate and interpret the resulting graph. They need to do this in several situations, so that their attention moves from the data and associated questions, to data handling as a technique. Thus, exposition can set the scene for personal exploration and reconstruction of ideas encountered fleetingly.

Exposition is sometimes seen as reinforcing both dependency on the teacher and the authority of that teacher. Being an authority, that is, being experienced or even expert in something is no bad thing either. Disaffection with exposition has to do with its being the sole mode of classroom interaction and with expertise turning into excessive control, leading to dependency. The teacher/expositor, knowing more about the topic, controls pupils' access to the ideas and techniques. Some degree of control is both needed and wanted if people are to learn. But the aim is to reduce the dependency on the teacher or expert as judge of correctness and source of ideas, while still using them to challenge and stimulate.* To achieve this, it is necessary to exploit interactions in which pupils explore and express themselves, whether through discussing, writing notes, drawing pictures and diagrams, making films, using computer programs or specifying calculator sequences.

Engaging in exposition is good for pupils as well as for teachers. Being stimulated to organize one's thoughts, to make real contact with the ideas in order to speak coherently about them to others plays a vital role in learning to express oneself on paper – something that pupils have to do ultimately to pass examinations.

Explaining

> The term *explaining* can be used to describe interactions with pupils in which the teacher tries to enter the pupils' world, tries to see things their way, to make 'plain' what the pupil is thinking and how that differs from what the teacher is thinking.

The words *explain* and *expound* are often used interchangeably. One reason is that *to explain* can mean both 'to make clear', and 'to justify' (to explain why, to explain oneself). But the two terms can also be used to distinguish distinct forms of telling which sometimes merge in classrooms, with unintended and unhelpful results.

---

* In the interlude which follows this chapter, the notions of *scaffolding* and *fading* will be introduced to pursue this matter further.

An explanation uses words and ideas already familiar to the pupil: it operates in the pupil's world. Whereas exposition typically introduces new ideas, explanation juxtaposes words already understood with terms whose meaning is uncertain or unclear, in order to help the pupil to be more certain as to their use and meaning.

When people 'explain how' to do something, it usually amounts to a demonstration: 'do this, then this, then this', which is actually much more like exposition, because pupils are invited to enter the demonstrator's world and do things 'that way'. The teacher outlines the steps, slowly and methodically, and the pupil is expected to copy. To explain something in the sense of justifying, of 'explaining why', it is necessary to root what is said in the audience's experience and this is the essence of explanation.

To explain something effectively to a pupil, it is essential to listen and, when speaking, to attend carefully to facial expressions and other body language. Effective explanation usually comes in short bursts. A long 'explanation' almost necessarily turns into exposition, because the speaker naturally slides into his own world, hoping that the pupil will follow. Once the explanation required comes to mind and the words start flowing fluently, it is very difficult to remain in the pupil's world.

It is often remarked that teachers who have recently struggled themselves with an idea are the best people to explain it to others, because they still have access to the pupils' world of difficulty. By contrast, the expert may have lost contact with the essential difficulties, may have become overly familiar with the ideas and relationships involved, and so finds it harder to explain and easier to expound.

Mathematical words, such as the language of probability or of subtraction, which seem entirely obvious and natural to the teacher, may appear to the pupil as unsupported and novel and the teacher's use may even contradict the pupils' own understanding. When the strange has become familiar, it is easy to forget the strangeness. What is succinctly stated by the expert may be difficult for a novice to take in all at once. Explanation involves re-experiencing strangeness and excitement through the pupil. A tour guide who is no longer fascinated by the scenery ceases to be effective. A teacher who ceases to be excited by mathematical results (or by pupils' excitement at discovering results) is in a similar position. Equally, a tour guide who is so fascinated by the scenery that contact with the audience is lost is ineffective.

One role of exposition is to inspire through generating surprise. To be effective in explaining, it is helpful to be able to experience the world of the pupil to recapture the state of surprise and wonder – even in topics which are very familiar. Any of the following mathematical facts can simply be asserted from a base of complete familiarity and a sense of 'it's obvious', yet each is an important part of the mathematics curriculum precisely because of the surprise it generated originally and its general applications in many different places. In each case the familiar can be experienced as strange:

It does not matter what order you count things in (provided you don't make a mistake) because you always get the same answer. *How amazing that independence of order is and it certainly doesn't hold when you are taking things away.*

The number after one thousand and ninety-nine is one thousand one hundred. *How powerful is the naming system, how mysteriously the numbers all receive not just one, but a variety of different names (6 also has the names 4 + 2, 30/5, √36, ...).*

The sum of any two even numbers is also even. *Amazing in its generality, since it covers such a vast range of cases.*

The π that comes from the circumference of any circle divided by the diameter is the same as the π that comes from the area divided by the square of the radius. *How remarkable that these two constants should be the same.*

A measurement made in one country when something is manufactured is the same when measured in the country of sale. *What is needed to ensure that different people make the same measurements?*

Despite considerable differences between individuals, there are trends in large numbers of people, such as preferences, opinions, height, etc. *How can one make a general statement that is accepted as correct and yet have it false in particular instances? How hard it is not to make such statements, say about people of other races, nationalities or cultural backgrounds.*

Nitsa Movshovits-Hadar (1988) suggests that by re-enthusing oneself, by re-experiencing the surprise or wonder at even the simplest of mathematical facts, it is possible to re-invigorate teaching and, at the same time, invigorate many pupils. By re-entering the state of mystery or excitement, by re-considering some problem or surprise which the ideas resolve, it is possible to awaken that same surprise in pupils.

Explanation, like exposition, plays an important part in being taught mathematics. If explanations do not come from somewhere, from the teacher or from each other, pupils may abandon hope altogether. Getting pupils to express things to each other is just one of the ways in which pupils can work at refining and honing what they understand and, in the process of explaining to someone else, learn. For this sort of activity to be successful, an appropriate classroom atmosphere, based on conjecturing, is essential.

Conjecturing

> A *conjecture* is an assertion which may be true, but which may need modification or even rejection in the light of further thought or evidence.

> A *conjecturing* atmosphere is one in which everything said is taken as a conjecture; in which pupils seek to express their thinking when they are unsure, and to listen carefully to each other when they are sure about the topic to hand.

Conjectures are usually expressions of patterns and regularities which a person perceives, expressed in words, pictures, symbols, or some other form. They cover a range of certainties from unsupported beliefs, through possibilities that seem intuitively correct, to assertions which the speaker believes can be justified by evidence and argument. Conjectures are most frequently intuitions which are changing into assertions.

Conjectures are a form of telling, in that offering a conjecture is a way of telling yourself, or someone else, what is currently believed to be the case, but in a way which suggests being open to considering modifications. In a conjecturing atmosphere, there is no need to tell someone that their answer is wrong. They may however be encouraged to reconsider their conjecture, to modify or amend it, and suggestions along these lines may be made by others. In a conjecturing atmosphere pupils are encouraged not to take assertions as facts, but to investigate matters for themselves.

There is a big difference between being told something and being told something which must subsequently be checked out against experience. The first type of telling brooks no argument, no questioning. The second is consistent with how mathematicians of all ages go about exploring with and in mathematics; as patterns are contemplated and examples catalogued, they form conjectures about what might be the case. Then further examples are examined in order to try to check that conjecture. Examples are sought which might disprove the conjecture or which might show why the idea will always work.

Conjectures are modified: they change and develop. They are part of what one tells oneself while exploring mathematically, yet they are often so fleeting and transitory that within moments it is hard to recall what it was that set a certain train of thought in motion. It is useful therefore to acknowledge utterances as conjectures and to note them down in a public place for later consideration. Working publicly this way reinforces the value in pupils doing the same thing when working individually or in small groups. Making a note of conjectures as they arise is worth while, because when a line of exploration is exhausted, there may be no other access to what prompted that direction apart from returning to the conjectures from which it originated. Writing conjectures down also helps if progress slows down or stops altogether because it is possible to go back and see recent thoughts and perhaps make a some changes or set off in a new direction. And if work is abandoned for a few minutes or days or years, it is much easier to come back to a conjecture than to rough notes. Furthermore, when time runs out, it is good mathematical practice to stop work with the current conjectures stated as clearly as possible, with a few notes about why the conjecture seemed reasonable. Not all questions that pupils consider can be resolved, but if they learn to suspend judgment, without looking for immediate resolutions, they will be better prepared to develop their thinking in the future.

Summary

Expounding is often frowned upon, yet in its highest form it can have a 'telling' effect. The audience may not be able to act differently but they may be more attuned to some possible ways of thinking or inspired to find out more. Pupils expound their ideas to each other and tell the teacher what they think are important facets of learning. To communicate a mathematical idea, it is essential to make mathematical contact, to summon up relevant and vivid mental images, to recall useful technical words and ideas that are related and to bring to mind the variety of different contexts in which the ideas occur to gain access to a world of experience connected with that topic.

Explaining involves entering the world of the listeners, making the thinking plain to them and to oneself, and offering additional and alternative versions to consider. Explanation often turns into exposition and one value in distinguishing between them as modes of telling is so that a transition is detectable while it is occurring, allowing a decision about which is likely to be the more effective mode to be made.

Exposition and explanation are both useful for setting up conditions in which exploration is appropriate, so that pupils have direction and purpose to their investigations.

Conjecturing involves externalizing thoughts which are in the process of being refined and made precise. It means being open to assistance in modifying and altering one's ideas. When a conjecturing atmosphere is established, pupils respond to exposition not as assertions to be 'learned' but as a stimulus to check out the ideas for themselves, to make sense for themselves through exploration and through explaining to each other.

Asking

In a classroom, a teacher asks 'What did I just ask you?' It may sound and look like a question, but is it? It could be:

- a genuine enquiry – the questioner having forgotten;
- exerting control by effectively asserting that the person was not listening;
- designed to focus attention on some mathematical process or idea;
- an indication of teacher frustration;
- a subtle working in the zone of proximal development.*

As with telling, the words alone do not enable a definitive analysis. A clue to the intention may given by the amount of time before the teacher's next intervention. There seems little point in asking a reflective question if time is not given for pondering, considering and conjecturing. By holding silence, by not fidgeting or allowing one's own thoughts to wander off to something else, pupil attention can be focused on the content of the question rather than just its form.

Instead of analysing what other people said, it may be more profitable to catch oneself in the act of asking a question and observing your intentions and experience 'from the inside'. Often the intention in asking a question emerges only in reaction to the response from the person questioned: a question is asked of pupils, pupils respond and the subsequent reaction highlights the original intention. For example:

> *The teacher notices a pattern of bricks in a wall. It occurs to her to ask pupils, 'What do you notice about the wall?'*

---

* This idea is due to Lev Vygotsky and is described more fully in the interlude following this chapter.

One pupil replies with talk about colours, another about the height, another about its age. The teacher's reaction 'What about the pattern?' or 'How many bricks do you think there are?' reveals the existence of a particular and definite focus.

> *A pupil is measuring with a ruler, but using the '1' mark as the starting-point. The teacher asks, 'What must you do when using a ruler?' and the pupil replies, 'Keep it still.'*

The teacher's reaction will reveal to both teacher and pupil what sort of a question was being asked.

> *In a secondary classroom, the task is to work out all the lengths of the sides and the sizes of the angles of a triangle given just some of them. The data have been accumulated on a diagram and the teacher, seeing that the law of cosines is the appropriate one to use, asks, 'Which is it to be, sines or cosines?'*

Pupils offer 'Sines', 'Cosines' and 'Measure them!' and the teacher's inner reaction to these suggestions reveals specific intentions in asking the initial question.

> *In a primary classroom, pupils are playing a domino-type game with logiblocks in which each new block added to the sequence has to match the last block in exactly two attributes. The teacher sees a pupil add an inappropriate block to the chain and asks, 'What are you matching for?'*

Pupils offer things like 'Colour', 'Colour and shape', 'It looks right' and the teacher's reaction reveals both to them and to the other pupils the original intentions of the question.

In each case, the actual response summons up a reaction and it is that reaction which is most informative about the original intention in asking the question.

It is a particular feature of adult–children interactions that adults will ask questions which would not be acceptable in a gathering of adults. Mehan (1986) has built an entire article around the apparently innocuous question, 'What time is it Denise?' So the reply, 'It's 2:30, Miss' is likely to get the response 'Thank you' at a railway station and 'Well done!' in an infant classroom. Many adults are exercised about adult–pupil questions, especially in the classroom* but pupils exhibit less concern and confusion about the difference between in- and out-of-school questioning than do researchers. Pupils seem to accept that they should be asked questions in school as part of the social practice of school.

Three aspects of asking

Researchers have delineated dozens of different forms of questions. We propose three aspects of asking questions as a suitable number to provide a sufficiently informative framework for making further investigations without being submerged in too many subtle distinctions.** Each form or mode takes into account

---

* See, for example, Valerie Walkerdine (1988) who adopts such a focus and through analysing extensive transcripts suggests that middle-class mothers ask many more teacher-like questions than do working-class mothers.

** The three forms proposed here correspond closely to the three forms identified independently by Ainley (1987).

not just the words uttered, but the intentions of the teacher, which in turn may only be revealed when a pupil responds and the teacher then reacts to that response.

Focusing

In the midst of a lesson, the teacher 'sees' something happening. For example:

- a pupil has generated a sequence of numbers such as 1, 4, 9, ... but does not seem to see the pattern of square numbers which leaps off the page at the teacher;

- pupils are measuring their heights and struggling to announce and record their results while a link back to earlier work on naming decimals is clear to the teacher;

- pupils are lost in details of measuring and cannot seem to see what calculations they need to do, yet to the teacher it is entirely obvious what they should do;

- pupils are trying to refer to different parts of a diagram and the teacher sees that they would be helped if they generated a notation or labelling to make it easier.

The teacher is aware of something which she thinks the pupil could also usefully be aware of. So she asks a question. Seeing a possibility generates a desire to say or do something to help the pupils and this usually emerges as a question rather than, for example, an instruction or suggestion. Take the situation, above, where the teacher sees a pattern in the number sequence but the pupil does not seem to. After each question the pupil offers little or no response, so another question is asked:

Can you see a pattern?

What is the same about this and this and this? (The teacher points to the individual terms)

What connections are there between this and this and this? (The teacher again points to the terms)

(Writing down the differences 3, 5, 7...) Do you recognize this sequence of numbers?

Will these numbers keep going up in odd numbers? Will you always get square numbers?

Heinrich Bauersfeld calls this sort of questioning sequence the *funnel effect*. Each time a pupil responds hesitantly, or not at all, the teacher feels drawn to be more precise, to ask something which the pupil will surely be able to answer.

John Holt (1964) describes an incident in which he eventually realized that the pupil had a strategy of saying almost nothing until Holt had refined and simplified the question until there was no risk in answering. Such situations arise when the questioner has a sharp sense of what they want the pupil to know/see/say, and it is all too easy to be sucked down the funnel by some form of 'guess what's in my mind' questioning. Familiarity plays a role in funnelling, for a pattern of routine questions, asked without much real thought, can create a sterile atmosphere which forces the teacher into more and more specific questions until teacher and/or pupil actually start thinking.

Funnelling in itself is neither good nor bad: rather its value depends on what teacher and pupil think is happening. If the teacher believes himself to be genuinely enquiring, or if the pupils wait for the questions to become more detailed and precise without working at the more diffuse and imprecise ones, then the interaction is likely to be a waste of time. If, on the other hand, the pupil is working hard at trying to relate ideas so that the funnelling helps focus attention in some unexpected or unfamiliar way, then the interaction could be fruitful.

The value of the term *funnelling* lies in the way it can come to mind in the midst of an interaction and so draw the teacher's attention out of the interaction details, and on to the nature of the interaction, thus providing a moment of choice: to continue down the funnel or to seek an alternative route or direction. A term such as funnelling is much more useful for observing one's own behaviour than it is for analysing other people's behaviour. In analysing transcripts and observing other teachers, it is easy to become obsessed with funnelling, or with 'guess what's in my mind', and to miss alternative interpretations. Almost any classroom interaction, any transcript or videotape of a lesson fragment can be interpreted as funnelling because of lack of information about what teacher and pupil are actually experiencing.

Although of increasing specificity, funnelling questions all have the same intention, namely to get the pupil to see what the teacher sees. Their purpose is to focus attention. If in the midst of interacting with pupils the teacher becomes aware of funnelling, of being driven by 'guess what's in my mind', there is an opportunity to pause, and to choose to continue or to back off or to indicate more directly to pupils the point of focus.

Focusing questions often arise in interactions to which Vygotsky's notion of the *zone of proximal development**** applies. For example, when pupils are working on a challenging task, the teacher may support their efforts by keeping track of the major goals, so that pupils can attend to the details. The following questions:

> *What was the question?*
>
> *What are you trying to do now?*
>
> *Does that calculation seem to be giving the sort of answer you expect?*

are all of this type, intended to pull pupils out of the details and to focus their attention on some global aspect. A teacher might use them to find out what the pupil is doing, so that the question helps both teacher and pupil to refocus. Such questions also serve to illustrate the way an internal mathematical-monitor might work. In the midst of a calculation, experts may find themselves asking 'Is this the right calculation?' Their internal monitors are relatively well developed. By way of contrast, a novice may be so deeply embedded in the calculation that he keeps on struggling, getting deeper and deeper into a mire, without any internal monitor to make him pause and step back from what he is doing to get an overall picture. Vygotsky was convinced that the only way such a monitor will develop is through social interactions with others whose monitors are active.

*   See the interlude following this chapter for details.

Focusing is a two-way activity. Teachers as experts are likely to be aware of connections, details and processes which the pupils do not see, but pupils are often aware of other features of questions and tasks, and it behoves a teacher to be sensitive to pupils' focus of attention and to try to enter that focus some of the time, as in the explanatory mode of the previous section.

Rehearsing

It is a common and natural part of teaching to ask questions which test pupils' knowledge, memory or awareness. For example:

> *What do we call a six-sided shape?*

> *What do you have to remember when using a protractor?*

> *How do you round a number to one decimal place?*

Here the teacher certainly knows the answer, but is trying to get the pupils to *rehearse* the answers for themselves. In *Maths Talk* (Mathematical Association, 1987) this is described as *checking up* and contrasted with *exploratory* questioning. It may be enough that pupils rehearse the words in their heads, though usually teachers like someone to give an answer so that everyone gets confirmation. Unfortunately this often has the effect that only the person answering pays much attention to the answer! At the beginning of a lesson, it is easy to want to 'just rehearse some of the ideas from last time' and to get caught up in a sequence of laconic, even sullen, responses from pupils. A large proportion of teacher questions are of the 'going over old ground' type. Rehearsal of terms and techniques is one good way to internalize ideas, to begin to employ them to express thoughts, rather than simply to repeat memorized phrases. But rehearsal need not always be initiated by questions:

> Whenever I am teaching, whether or no I am working on the board, I like each boy to have beside him a sheet of scrap paper; on that he can write down the answer to any question which I ask the class generally, or he can attempt the next step of the work which I am doing on the board, or draw the figure for himself …

> This serves two purposes: first, if a boy is liable to be called on at any moment to write down an answer or do the next step of a piece of work being done on the board, he must pay active attention and need not merely look interested; secondly, if he makes a mistake he knows that he has done so, or if he is uncertain of a step he is aware of it, and consequently he is much more likely to ask a question about it and get it cleared up at once

> *(Siddons in Godfrey and Siddons, 1931, quoted in Brissenden, 1980)*

For example, the teacher can weave a story about animals or people based on ideas on a collection of cards with mathematical terms and objects on them. Pupils can then make up their own story or even tell a collective story. In primary classrooms, such stories are likely to be about animals, with the teacher providing structural elements such as teddy bears of different sizes, wiggly worms of different lengths, and other stuffed animals, which need to be measured for clothes and food requirements as in squirrels checking their supply of nuts (and so needing to count them) and so on (Mathematical Association, 1987). In secondary classrooms the stories are likely to be more topical (see, for example Hopkins, 1990). Secondary pupils can also be challenged to write instructions to a friend or to a pupil in another class or to someone who has been ill, about how to do a certain 'type' of question. Here the activity of rehearsing is invoked without asking a direct, rehearsing-type of question.

Ainley (1987) points out that asking questions to which one already knows the answer is a cultural phenomenon associated with the European idea of school teaching. Aboriginal children in Australia come from a culture in which it is considered ill mannered to ask a direct question, so to ask a question to which one already knows the answer is thought to be bizarre! Constant questioning and extending the limits of knowledge of younger people may be typical of middle-class interaction patterns, rather than endemic to society as a whole.

And yet it is hard to imagine not asking questions which stimulate pupils to rehearse, to reconstruct what they know, in the sense of Dewey. Where pupils perceive questions as testing rather than as opportunities for rehearsing, for 'explaining to themselves' but out loud in the presence of others, they may be confined by tensions and concerns about getting things right rather than being open to opportunities to get things not quite right and then to modify and correct them. Rehearsing need not be a burden but, in parallel with the bad press which exposition has received, getting pupils to exercise new techniques or ideas on examples is sometimes thought to be incompatible with an investigative approach to mathematics. In order to be able to reconstruct ideas from their own experience, pupils need opportunities to rehearse those ideas, to try to explain things to others. They also need to automate techniques and this can be done both on routine exercises and through explorations which call upon those techniques. For example, board games which involve pupils in counting serve to exercise counting while attention is focused on the game; trying to find a quadratic expression with given roots or whose roots have a given sum and product serves to exercise factoring while attention is directed toward a larger goal.

The widespread popularity of Trivial Pursuits, Mastermind and similar quizzes, attests to the challenge that some people get from a series of testing questions. It is an opportunity for them to rehearse what they know, in public, so it must be possible to set up similar conditions in classrooms. But testing can gain the upper hand and start to drive teaching, so that the teacher and then the pupils focus on what will be in the test, not on encountering the subject matter.

Enquiring

A third form of questioning is called by some, the 'true' or 'genuine' question where information is genuinely sought. For example:

> *What were you thinking of when you wrote that down? (referring to something in a piece of pupil work)*
>
> *How did you get that?*
>
> *Can you put something on the paper lid so that you can remember how many beans are in it?*

However, genuineness depends as much on the teacher's intention as it does on the words used. Most of the examples above can be interpreted as focusing or as rehearsal or as some form of classroom control, rather than as genuine enquiry. For example, if a teacher asks a pupil:

> *What do you see in the picture?*

the intention could be a genuine enquiry, meaning:

> *I am interested in what you see and I cannot know unless you tell me.*

When the teacher is seeking information the question-situation can be labelled as *enquiring*. To stimulate pupils to enquire, it is at least useful, if not essential, to provide a model of enquiring. Simulating interest is not enough because pupils will soon see through any pretence. Although it is not always easy to remain in a state of genuine enquiry about the mathematical content of some pupils' work, it is possible to be genuinely interested in how pupils are thinking, in how they express themselves, in what they see in their heads. Teachers who are evidently interested in their pupils are more likely to generate and support an enquiring attitude in them.

The trouble with using questions to enquire is that even a question such as 'What do you see in the picture?' could be intended to, or interpreted as an attempt to, focus attention without being directive:

> *I have something in mind that I see. Do you see it too?*

or even to test:

> *You are supposed to be attuned to seeing what I am seeing. Are you?*

As with other forms of questioning, it is the follow-up reactions which signal both to teacher and pupil what sort of an interaction is intended.

The adjective 'genuine' is unfortunate because in a classroom questions are part of a power structure in which the teacher's aim is to evaluate the pupil's understanding so as to be of further assistance and also because it implies that other forms of question are fake, misleading or in some way of lesser value. Some people use the term 'genuine' as a value judgement, implying that all questions should or could be 'genuine'. A question is not rendered fake or 'ungenuine' simply because it is deployed for rehearsal or focusing purposes. All three forms of questioning have their place in classroom practice. A particular form of questioning is problematic only if teacher and pupils are unclear or at odds about what sort of questioning is taking place. If pupils are in the habit of interpreting all teacher questions as *testing*, then work has to be done to show them that there are indeed other opportunities being offered, other types of questioning.

On reacting and responding to pupils

> *If you don't know your pupils well, then it is difficult to know how to respond to what they say and do. If you know your pupils well, then you can respond to them individually, through that knowledge.*

These sentiments seem entirely plausible and yet there are some difficulties. This section concerns a distinction between *reacting* to pupils, that is, automatically following some habituated pattern of behaviour in reaction to pupils' behaviour and to what is known about them and *responding* to pupils, that is, approaching what the pupil says and does without prejudice. The distinction is subtle, but nonetheless potentially important.

In getting to know individuals it is very difficult not to develop habits. The first few days and weeks of a new year or the first few weeks in a new school are critical because it is during this time that pupil- and teacher-expectations develop. Each works out what the other demands and what the other is not fussed about. Thus, one teacher may be a stickler for how notebooks are used, another for how pupils come into the classroom and settle down to work, another that pupils not call out without putting their hands up. One may work at establishing a working atmosphere in which the teacher is not to be disturbed unless the pupil cannot get help from someone at their table; another may require all questions to come to her. The habits or norms of a classroom are quickly established, and once in place, quite difficult to alter.

A wide range of reactions quickly become established:

- the pupil who sits at the back of a classroom, or in a corner, and whose table is often noisy;
- the pupil who always seems to be borrowing things from neighbours;
- the pupil who seems shy and reticent;
- the pupil who always has something to say;
- the pupil who giggles.

Some or all of these are present in every classroom. But notice that the descriptions given say that the pupil is like this or like that. Already a step has been taken towards labelling or characterizing the pupil. The teacher's response to such behaviour quickly develops into a reaction to the pupil.

Teaching is an enormously complex task. To be aware of all the dimensions at any one moment is impossible, much less at every moment during the day. So it is essential to develop standard ways of dealing with outbursts of noise, lack of concentration, getting activity started, getting pupils reflecting on what they have done, and so on. Without strongly embedded and developed habits, it would be impossible to survive in a classroom. Unfortunately, this creates a tension, because it is precisely in the automatic, habituated reactions that stereotyping develops.

- Some pupils often get labelled as class jokers. The image that others have reinforces this behaviour and makes it difficult for them to be taken seriously, so the serious side of their natures may not get developed.
- Pupils who seem to struggle with new ideas or with symbols or with physical coordination or with expressing themselves fluently get labelled as *low attaining*, *slow* or even *low ability*. The label generates habitual re-actions, so that flashes of brilliance even go unrecognized. Teachers start making things easier for such pupils, by breaking things down into smaller steps, and effectively maintaining the label which has been applied to the pupil. Pupil and teacher end up colluding or contriving

together to maintain the labels. At least everyone knows where they are, socially, even if they do not like it.

- A distinction between boys and girls is perfectly natural. But it is easy to develop different reactions to pupils simply on the basis of gender. Researchers have noticed that boys who ask questions more often get a question in reply than do girls; that boys and girls are often asked different types of questions; that disruptive behaviour from boys is excused 'because they are boys' while disruptive behaviour from girls is stamped on. Again, there is a potentially self-feeding loop of behaviour from the pupil and reaction from the teacher, both based on expectations and labels, which helps to support and continue the stereotyped images and expectations.

- A pupil with 'outlandish' hair-style or clothes generates a reaction which differs from reactions to more 'normal' appearance. It is very tempting to associate intelligence and interest with outer appearances. Such 'conjectures' can be quickly affirmed and validated because of the need to react quickly in teaching encounters with pupils. Once established, they may be hard to change.

- Pupils with different racial or ethnic backgrounds from one's own or for whom English is not the first language, can very easily become associated with certain expectations. Subsequent interactions usually seem to confirm those prejudgments, those prejudices, making it very hard to see past one's own expectations.

Automatic, habitual reactions are, as has been suggested, entirely natural, especially in a busy classroom where there is little time for thought before speaking or consideration of various viewpoints when the flow of a lesson is interrupted.

It is entirely reasonable to form expectations of what pupils can do and not to waste time setting overly challenging activities which then require a lot of support from the teacher. And yet at the same time, the expectations, the labels that pupils receive (often tacitly rather than explicitly) and the reactions which such labels then produce, may have as much to do with pupil 'success', as anything else that happens in lessons. In a famous research study (see Rosenthal and Jacobsen, 1968), researchers set up teacher expectations about different children which were entirely unrelated to pupils' past performance and pupils seemed on the whole to respond according to the teacher's expectations.

So what can be done? How can the tension between the need to react and the desire to respond be used to advantage rather than disadvantage? The suggestion being made here is that by being aware, in the moment, of a distinction between *reacting* and *responding*, it may be possible, occasionally, to choose rather than to react automatically.

Summary

It has been suggested that teacher–pupil interactions involve a variety of forms of telling and asking. A pedagogy based solely on exposition ('This is what it's about'), example ('This is how you do it') and exercises ('Now you practise it') is no more and no less deadening than a pedagogy based solely on exploration ('Here's an activity to get started on') and writing up ('Write about what you did and what you found out'). As with telling people things, asking questions is only problematic when questioner or questioned misconstrues what the intentions of the questioner are; when it is assumed that questions asked become genuine questions, which evoke a considered response rather than simply a reaction. When pupils interpret all questions as testing, as seeking a correct answer, they are likely to focus on getting or giving the correct answer and this will inhibit the establishment of a conjecturing atmosphere.

It is natural for reactions to what pupils say to become habitual and automatic but this reduces the opportunities to respond freshly and to see what pupils are really thinking. Labelling pupils by their reactions can produced habitual responses in them.

Mathematical discussion

Since teachers ask most of the questions in lessons, it is understandable that pupils usually respond to the teacher. The trouble with this is that many pupils will attend closely to what the teacher says but ignore what fellow pupils say. In order to get constructive dialogue, so that pupils can work productively together with or without the teacher, it is usually necessary to spend time in training pupils in listening and discussion.

Reports of lessons often include 'We discussed ...', but observation of such lessons reveals that the teacher told the pupils a few things and perhaps asked a few questions to which pupils gave at most succinct answers. This sort of 'discussion' is not what we mean by mathematical discussion.

Can mathematics actually be discussed in the more general use of the term? How can you have opinions in mathematics?

If discussion is seen as a mode of interaction in which individuals try to express their ideas, and through expressing them come to a better understanding, then mathematical discussion is indeed possible. It provides an opportunity for pupils to distance themselves from their own ideas, to become articulate about their insights, to examine their ideas and intuitions critically and to make modifications supported by the suggestions of colleagues. In the process, it releases the teacher from having to be present all the time.* Learning *can* take place without the teacher!

In order to accomplish this distancing, pupils need to struggle to express their own thinking and to listen to and learn from the thinking of others. They need to learn to listen sympathetically but critically, to ask questions and to offer alternative conjectures. This sort of behaviour is possible at all ages but it does not

---

* Recent studies of discussion have often made use of a computer as a source of what to discuss. See, for example, Healy, Hoyles and Sutherland (1990).

happen overnight. It requires careful development, even training in listening and pondering and in speaking clearly enough for others to hear and make sense. It also requires the teacher to have confidence in what she is doing and to be seen to put confidence in the pupils. For example, it is quite difficult to generate discussion simply by asking a question until pupils are experienced in discussion techniques and are willing to open up and offer their ideas. And it is not often sensible to embark on a free-flowing discussion without having considered in advance the ideas likely to arise. It is essential to be attuned to the kinds of language patterns that pupils are likely to use and to be sensitive to the sorts of images and awarenesses which prompt pupils to say what they do. If the teacher decides in advance where the discussion will lead there is a risk of having not discussion but question and answer. There is a delicate balance to be achieved between preparation and spontaneity.

Pirie and Schwarzenberger set out a list of possible requirements for a mathematical discussion:

> *It is purposeful talk* i.e., there are well-defined goals even if not every participant is aware of them. These goals may have been set by the group or by the teacher, but they are, implicitly or explicitly, accepted by the group as a whole.
>
> *on a mathematical subject* i.e., either the goals themselves, or a subsidiary goal which emerges during the course of the talking, are expressed in terms of mathematical content or process.
>
> *in which there are genuine pupil contributions* i.e., input from at least some of the pupils which assists the talk or thinking to move forwards. We are attempting here to distinguish between the introduction of new elements to the discussion and mere passive response, such as factual answers, to teachers' questions.
>
> *and interaction* i.e., indications that the movement within the talk has been picked up by other participants. This may be evidenced by changes of attitude within the group, by linguistic clues of mental acknowledgement, or by physical reactions which show that critical listening has taken place, but *not* by mere instrumental reaction to being told what to do by the teacher or by another pupil.

(Pirie and Schwarzenberger, 1988, p. 461)

Maria Bartolini-Bussi (1990), in working with mathematics teachers over a three-year period, identified three types of mathematical discussion: discussion *before*, *within* and *after* work on a topic.

Before: usually short discussions as they involve pupils in discussing how they see the task or question which has been presented. It can also involve collecting together pupils' ideas and associations with a topic before getting down to pre-arranged activity, as in asking pupils what they know about π, or about cutting things into portions; the purpose being to remind pupils of what they already know that is related to the topic at hand.

Within: discussion that arises between pupils as they explore a suggestion or work on an activity. It is not easy to 'manage' because it is spontaneous and although it plays an important social role in the individual pupil's construction of meaning, it is not easy to see what aspects are most important and what aspects peripheral to understanding.

For example, it is often the case that a pupil who says little actually understands a lot while a pupil who talks a lot may not actually be listening or even working very hard at making sense! A pupil who seems to be using the words in incorrect or misguided ways may actually be sorting out what they mean, while another who uses the words correctly may actually be repeating them from memory* rather than expressing their current ideas.

After: this sort of discussion is an impetus to reflect, to try and relate ideas together into some sort of 'story' of what the topic is about.

It is often the case that time is seen as an enemy, that tiredness takes over, and so reflection is omitted. Yet if the teacher is not seen to value such activity, pupils will also tend to devalue it and the whole point of a series of lessons may be largely wasted.

Bartolini-Bussi also suggests that the teacher has two major roles to play when present in a discussion (and hence in training the pupils for when she is not present), namely as *moderator* of the interactions and as *mediator* of the mathematical ideas. The moderator makes sure that people are listening, deflects attention away from herself and stimulates pupils to listen to each other, to question and to modify what is said. The mediator is available to help with technical terms, to introduce examples which may require more thought but which the pupils might not find for themselves.

It might be expected that getting pupils discussing ideas among themselves would throw up disagreements and conflicts which would in turn lead to resolution and hence learning, with or without recourse to the teacher. But is is clear that discussion itself, being a social interaction, will not necessarily reveal disagreements and, even if it does, may not provide any support for reconciling those disagreements. Furthermore, pupils may confirm mistakes rather than correct them or may even develop new ones. Must the teacher be present for correct learning to occur? Certainly there is more to it than simply putting pupils in groups and getting them to discuss (see, for example, Brissenden, 1988).

Alan Bell and his colleagues (Bell, 1986, Bell, Brekke and Swann,1987a, 1987b, 1987c; Bell and Purdy, 1986) in common with other authors (for example Scott, 1990) propose that one fruitful way to generate discussion is to reverse the usual kind of exercise-questions which pupils are asked to do when they are practising a skill for mastery. Thus:

- instead of 'What is 2×3?' ask 'What question could give 6 as an answer?'
- instead of 'What is $\frac{2}{3} + \frac{4}{5}$?' tell pupils that someone got the answer $\frac{6}{8}$ but that it was marked wrong, and ask them what they think the pupil did and why was it incorrect.

---

* With repeating from memory the important thing is that, in becoming familiar with using technical terms and stock phrases, those terms grow in meaning for the pupil; compare this with scaffolding where the most important thing is the removal of the scaffolding – the *fading*, see the interlude following this chapter.

- instead of asking pupils to put 0.234, 0.56 and 0.7 in order of increasing size, tell them that when pupils are asked to do it, some pupils say 0.234 is the largest, even though it is smaller than 0.56, and then ask why pupils might do this.

In each case, pupils' attention is being drawn to a difficulty which they may themselves have. By offering it for discussion and by giving pupils a chance to explain how they think about it, they are encouraged to expose and distance themselves from erroneous or incomplete thinking and thereby make it more likely that they can correct their own thinking.

Summary

Mathematical discussion involves pupils taking opportunities to express what they are seeing and thinking to the teacher and to each other. It is not the mathematical facts that are 'up for discussion' in the sense of negotiation but rather the pupils' thinking, their constructions and ideas which embed those facts and give them meaning. Discussion is a way to support pupils, individually and collectively, in developing confidence in mathematical ideas and the language used to express those ideas. To express oneself effectively calls upon mental imagery, in saying what one sees, vividly and succinctly, to others. This may also involve the use of objects, pictures and symbols, so that all aspects of mathematical thought are supported and strengthened.

Frames and assumptions

A lesson is more than a collection of interactions and the forms of interaction which develop depend on pupil and teacher expectations and aims and on personal propensities and they are influenced by school ethos, by the weather and by a myriad of other seemingly innocuous factors.

The purpose of offering frames for ways of considering classrooms and lesson preparation, such as three forms of asking or three forms of telling, is not to state how things should, or even could, be done. Rather, it is to offer a structure, something against which to examine one's own assumptions. The purpose is to provide a jolt, either through reaction against or through resonance with what is offered. The jolt may stimulate a re-thinking of classroom behaviour and an attempt to try to describe one's own particular pedagogical styles. In the process of bringing them to the surface they can be juxtaposed against what others have suggested from their experience.

The frames presented in the previous sections reflect a certain perspective, certain assumptions and ways of thinking about mathematics itself, and about teaching and learning it.

In this chapter, we have expounded some ideas, at a global level, not by analysing transcripts of interactions, but by abstracting from classroom experience and trying to write in a form which will resonate with experience. This assumes that our writing will indeed speak to your experience. We have also accentuated the role of the individual teacher and their own psychology, rather than, for example, the social role of peer group interactions. We have focused on verbal interactions and not on classroom organization or schemes of work.

An underlying assumption which justifies our choices is that change and development come about largely by individuals noticing opportunities and taking affirmative action to try out fresh responses and the frames are intended to assist in that process.

At a more detailed level, our emphasis on verbal interactions suggests a perspective in which the teacher is a critical component of the mathematics classroom not simply a recorder of work done and a marker of scripts. This is not universally assumed as pressures mount to teach more pupils with fewer teachers and to develop computer-based technologies which can support mathematics learning without a teacher for some of the time.

What else could have been emphasized? Of considerable, if not equal importance to personal psychology, is the role of the community of mathematics teachers and particularly of colleagues who are encountered each day. As a group, there are communal assumptions about children and about mathematics, and it is a rare teacher who takes a stance different from the norm and yet remains comfortably within a particular school.

We could also have offered more detailed distinctions based on research studies which identified ten or more types of teacher–pupil interaction or seven types of classroom questioning. Most people find three things an optimal number to remember. We chose to offer a few distinctions which could prove fruitful in noticing things happening in the classroom which might previously have become habitual. Our distinctions may then be modified or rejected in favour of others. What matters is that awareness is enriched, opportunities increased and choices made possible.

Interlude
On readiness and fading

There is no point in telling someone something, or in trying to teach it to them in some other way, if they are not yet ready for it.

The notion of *readiness* seems entirely reasonable. It would be foolish to attempt to teach fractions to two-year-olds and if an idea is not accessible then there is little point in wasting energy and time and getting frustrated by inflicting it upon them. Yet everyone, young and old alike, encounters things that they do not understand and it is through those encounters that they gain the experience necessary for coming to understand later. For example, young children often show that they make sense of adult conversation, including complex sentences and vocabulary, even though they cannot themselves participate; indeed before children speak they usually have a period in which they seem to make sense of what is said to them, even though they cannot yet say words or sentences back. Where children are exposed to adult conversation, rather than just child-oriented language, their vocabulary and thinking processes sometimes develop more quickly; where children participate with older children their development is often accelerated: a second-born often learns to speak at an earlier age than a first-born.

Children learn to position themselves *as children* through verbal and physical interactions with adults. They position themselves *as pupils* through interactions with adults, particularly in adopting the social and language conventions of the classroom. They not only learn language, but through language learn about their roles. Bronwyn Davies (1989) undertook detailed studies of pre-school children and concluded that masculinity and femininity are as much socialized positions as they are physiological. Young children learn to be masculine or feminine through participating in and rehearsing the language patterns which define and support them.

Arguably the same positioning takes place with respect to intellectual achievement. Swots and athletes, low and high attainers, being 'with it' and 'not with it' are all positions produced and maintained through a combination of social pressures and individual propensities.

Faced with a room full of children with different needs and dispositions, it is entirely natural, for example, to simplify one's speech so that all will understand, and as a result, unintentionally impoverish the experience of most, if not all, pupils. Deciding on the readiness and abilities of individual pupils and labelling them as such can mean shutting oneself off from seeing other strengths and potential development, and from having to search out particular difficulties which individuals are having, perhaps through having construed some ambiguity in a novel way. Deciding that a pupil 'needs' to be taken back to earlier work can exercise the desire to teach under the guise of helping, while insulating the teacher from the harder task of entering the pupils' experience and truly explaining.* Teachers often report that after a visitor has worked with their class some

---

* Valerie Walkerdine (1988) emphasizes this point in her analysis of teacher–pupil transcripts.

normally reticent pupils respond vigorously and other normally outspoken children remain quiet, suggesting that labelling pupils as 'responsive' or 'able' is mistaking their response to one teacher in a few instances for their innate qualities.

Motivated by a desire to simplify the design of instruction, it is all too easy to turn the notion of readiness into a principle which results in failure to stimulate, challenge and extend pupils sufficiently thereby inhibiting rather than promoting learning. By declaring a pupil not ready for something it is possible to cut them off from experiences which lay the foundation for future readiness.

The idea of readiness derives from, or was taken up by developmental psychologists and then crystallized by educationalists designing forms of instruction to take account of what psychologists found. In attempting to generate working principles, many fell prey to a metaphor of steady growth, of making the steps small enough so that pupils could climb the staircase of knowledge without travail. The metaphor may be compelling but it is ultimately inappropriate. For example, young children learn their parents' tongue by hearing it and by trying to use it. But they do not learn through steady development. They often go through periods of rigid behaviour patterns (over-general use of nouns, improper use of pronouns, incorrect past tenses of irregular verbs, etc.) and, despite repeated correction or criticism, appear to disregard completely the opinions of others. Then suddenly they switch and act completely differently. Something similar happens later with preferences for certain food, music, clothes, companions, etc. It is as if their attention has been fully occupied elsewhere but, none the less, they have been listening at some level all along.

The notion of readiness was sensitively used by Maria Montessori in Italy at the turn of the century in her mathematical work with deprived children. She recommended repeatedly offering children opportunities. If these were not taken up immediately, then instead of abandoning the idea, or labelling the children as *unable*, she advocated exposure to those same opportunities at intervals until they were indeed taken up. Her ideas were similar to those of John Dewey in America at about the same time who promulgated the view of education as drawing out the powers and talents of pupils in contrast to the prevailing images of the mind as a *tabula rasa* and teaching as 'bucket filling'.

Dewey saw education as the reconstruction of accumulated experience by each individual, the teacher's role being to provide the opportunities and stimulate the reconstruction. In other words, whatever is said to pupils they can only add what they hear to their store of experiences and try to construct their own stories about how it all fits together.

The ideas of Jean Piaget in Switzerland are better known, or more widely recognized, than those of Dewey but draw upon similar roots. He coined the term *genetic epistemology** to express something similar to Dewey's notion of recon-

---

* *Genetic*, in the sense of genesis, of 'becoming', and *epistemology* meaning 'theory of knowledge', so *genetic epistemology* is the study of how knowledge and ways of knowing develop over time. Some mathematics educators have also interpreted *genetic epistemology* as suggesting that pupils have in-built, genetic ways of finding out, of coming to know, of making sense of the world, in which pupils are seen as sense-making agents not buckets to be filled.

struction. He saw thinking as action, at first upon objects, then on language about objects, then on ideas using objects, and finally on ideas without objects: a process of de-objectification which constitutes the pupil's making sense of experience.

Emphasis in governmental reports on the use of practical apparatus to assist pupils to encounter mathematical ideas derives from all three of these thinkers. Unfortunately, rather less emphasis is placed on encouraging people to reduce their dependency on physical objects when thinking mathematically and to gain facility with mental images and abstract ideas independent of physical objects.

When global views of education are turned into practice, all manner of perturbations and simplifications are likely. There is a difference between returning to an idea every so often to see if a child responds, as Montessori advocated, and declaring that pupils of a certain age are not ready or not able to encompass some idea. Many of the teaching projects based on applying theoretical and psychological ideas assumed that if pupils did not respond as intended, they were not at the appropriate stage of readiness. Tasks were classified according to stage, much as ideas were assigned to levels in the national curriculum for England and Wales in the 1990s. Thus, the narrow notion of stages of development and readiness have contributed to the syndrome of 'keep it simple for them because they may not yet be ready' which is endemic in texts and schemes.

The Russian psychologist Lev Vygotsky offered a perspective which can make *readiness* a more useful idea. He stressed the role of language in learning and particularly the social role of other people in the development and use of language. He suggested that the higher psychological functions, such as performing complex tasks and monitoring what one is doing, are derived from internalizing the behaviour observed in others during social interactions. Thus, he emphasized the importance of getting pupils talking about their thinking in order to help them make sense of, or construct, mathematical and social meaning. For example, by arranging activities in which different aspects of the task are distributed among several people so that each is induced to speak about their contribution, mental actions which might otherwise be hidden are made explicit and so available for internalization.

Vygotsky observed that there are differences between what a pupil can achieve working alone, what they can achieve when working with other pupils and what they can achieve when assisted by someone more experienced, such as a teacher. He captured this in a phrase, which in English is usually rendered by *zone of proximal development*.* It describes the conceptual and social developments which are potentially imminent for pupils or, in other words, their sensitivities and readiness to develop. Integral to this idea is the necessity of the actions to be distributed among two or more people.** The pupils do what they can and the

---

* *Proximal* as in 'next' or 'nearby', with the same root as *approximate* and as *proximity*; *zone* is meant to indicate a range or variety of possibilities. In Russian, *zone* has much less of the sense of a well defined region of space than it does in English, so it is worth not over emphasising the implied spatial metaphor. For the elaboration of a similar idea, the notion of a *frontier zone* between confident functioning and inability to function, where functioning is uncertain and unreliable, see Richard Skemp (1979).

** For Vygotsky this was always the pupil and the teacher.

teacher acts to augment and extend what the pupils do.

Jerome Bruner, who introduced Vygotsky's ideas to the West, describes a teacher working 'in the zone of proximal development'.

> … she turned the task into play and caught it in a narrative that gave it continuity.
>
> What emerged was, I suppose, obvious enough. She was indeed 'consciousness for two' for the three- and five-year-olds she tutored, and in many ways. To begin with, it was she who controlled the focus of attention. It was she who, by slow and often dramatized presentation, demonstrated the task to be possible. She was the one with a monopoly on foresight. She kept the segments of the task on which the child worked to a size and complexity appropriate to the child's powers. She set things up in such a way that the child could *recognize* a solution and perform it later even though the child could neither do it on his own nor follow the solution when it was simply *told* to him. In this respect, she made capital out of the 'zone' that exists between what people recognize or comprehend when present before them, and what they can generate on their own. … In general, what the tutor *did* was what the child could *not* do. For the rest, she made things such that the child could do *with* her what he plainly could not do *without* her. And as the tutoring proceeded, the child took over from her parts of the task that he was not able to do at first but, with mastery, became consciously able to do under his own control. And she gladly handed those over.
>
> *(Bruner, 1986, pp. 75–6)*

The pupil is seen to take over those actions which they are ready to take over. Bruner goes on to observe that when children teach other children, their behaviour is similar except that they tend not to hand over those parts of the task which the younger child is beginning to be able to do. It is a most salutary exercise to see how children elect to teach friends about some topic or idea that has been missed because the children do not always mirror what the teacher thinks she is doing.

The concept of a *zone of proximal development* can be useful for describing a number of different ways in which the teacher extends or supports pupil awareness. Brown and Ferrera (1985) suggested that 'by interacting with an adult who guides problem solving activity and structures the learning environment, the child gradually comes to adopt the structuring and regulatory activities as his own' (p. 278).

For example:

- A teacher can keep track of the overall direction of an exploration, while pupils are embedded in the details.

- A teacher can be aware of mathematical thinking processes and remind pupils of them at times judged to be appropriate while pupils are caught up in the thinking.

- A teacher can be aware of the social interactions in a group and act to ease or structure the way of working so that time is spent productively while pupils are engaged in the social interaction.

Issues of control and causation are inescapable. Not every child will adopt the structuring offered by the teacher and the teacher has to guard against imposing rigidity rather than stimulating pupils to use some sort of structure. There is no easy solution to a teaching-tension such as this. To offer no structure is to abrogate one's responsibility as a teacher; to impose rigid structure is to train rather than to educate.

In presenting Vygotsky's ideas in English, Bruner (in Wood *et al.*, 1976) introduced the notion of *scaffolding* to refer to the assistance that a teacher can give at one time, which can be gradually withdrawn as the pupil is able to function independently. The image is of scaffolding which is erected temporarily while the shell of a building is erected and which is then removed. Vygotsky's idea of *zone of proximal development* suggests that by means of *scaffolding*, the teacher wants to support awareness that is imminent but not yet available to the pupil and not to do those things which the pupil can do perfectly well, since this will only promote dependency. The critical part of *scaffolding** is its removal or *fading* (see Brown *et al.*, 1989). For example, when a teacher interacts with pupils who are deeply involved in some calculations, reminding them that only a rough estimate is needed, or prompting them to go back and think again about the original question, or suggesting that they be systematic in trying some special cases, does not in and of itself constitute *scaffolding*. The notion of a zone of proximal development applies only if, over a period of time, there is a fading away of the prompts, so that the *zone* shifts and the pupils spontaneously take up what was previously prompted. Direct reminders and interventions can gradually be replaced with indirect prompts, such as 'What did I suggest yesterday?' or 'What strategy did you use last week for something similar?', and ultimately aiming for spontaneous use (adoption) by pupils of prompts, questions, heuristics and process-awareness that the teacher currently provides. Only then, when the support has been removed, is it sensible to use the metaphor of scaffolding as a description of how a teacher interacted with pupils. Otherwise, what was intended to be scaffolding may turn into the skeleton of the building: the pupil may become dependent upon the teacher.

Perhaps, then, the most important contribution towards the notion of *readiness*, is the idea of *fading*, of gradually withdrawing interventions of one type, and providing interventions of another type, so that pupils are being challenged to reconstruct accumulated experience (in the sense of Dewey) rather than to wait for teacher to tell them what to do next. So telling people something, in expository or explanatory mode, can be of positive assistance, as long as what is said or explained is at the edges of what pupils can do for themselves, rather than in the core. Instead of trying to make things easier for pupils who are struggling with an idea, it may be more effective to locate an appropriate challenge to augment or extend their attention, so that they can accomplish more temporarily but then to fade that assistance as they are called upon to become more independent.

---

* See Jaworski (1990) for an elaboration of some of the implications of the scaffolding metaphor on pupil dependency on teachers.

Chapter 3
Activity and planning

Perspectives on pupils' activity

We start with three anecdotes from mathematics lessons.

> *The teacher stands at the board on which there is a drawing of two triangles. He identifies one of these as acute angled, the other as obtuse. By asking questions he further reminds the class, drawing more diagrams as needed, of the meanings of the terms 'isosceles', 'equilateral', 'scalene'. He asks the class to open their books at page 37 (where there are twenty numbered triangles drawn) and tells them to work through that page, 'Put the numbers in your exercise books and write the correct word against each one.' The class settles to work and continues, with very little said, for about ten minutes.*

◇   ◇   ◇

> *Darren is working at a task set by his teacher. It involves using a computer program to find the treasure hidden on a coordinate grid. After each attempt a clue is given, which shows the distance of his current choice from the treasure. Darren enters pairs of coordinates on the computer and eventually finds the treasure, moves on to another turn and does the same again. He is apparently acting correctly: entering pairs of coordinates on the computer, continuing until he finds the treasure. But when the teacher questions Darren she discovers that he has been ignoring the clues and his coordinates are guesses, more or less at random. For the teacher this misses the point of the task*

– her intention is not that children will guess at random but that they will, by reflecting on their choices and the clues, devise a strategy for finding the treasure.

◇　　◇　　◇

The teacher stands at the board and outlines a problem he wants the class to work at. The twenty-five fifteen- and sixteen-year-olds are sitting in twos and threes around tables. The problem concerns finding the areas of triangles with one corner at the origin and two of whose sides are given by their position vectors. The diagram drawn by the teacher looks like this:

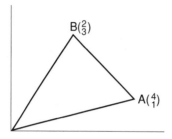

The teacher reminds the class that they know some methods for finding areas. One girl offers, 'You put a square round it'. The teacher acknowledges what she said but makes no further comment. After a little more explanation the class start to settle to work. One boy says to the teacher, 'I don't know what a vector is'.

Each of these three anecdotes concerns the setting of tasks for children and what happens as a result. From the first, we wish to draw attention to a commonly-used lesson structure; the second points to an activity not going as planned; the third raises issues about what the purpose of a task might be.

Pupils are given tasks by teachers to get them to engage in activities that will result in learning. Both the planning and the management of activities takes place against a background of the externally-defined mathematics curriculum throughout the years of schooling. Government curriculum guidelines are further reinterpreted by the authors of schemes but teachers will view both of these through their own beliefs about the development of children and progression through the curriculum and inevitably provide their own interpretations. How teachers think of the tasks they give the pupils and how they instigate activities in the light of the curriculum are the foci of this chapter.

When teachers plan a task, what types of activity do they want to encourage? What kinds of learning might particular tasks foster? How do teachers decide whether and in what ways to augment or modify activities? When an activity is felt to be successful or when one fails, what features have contributed to this?

We examine these aspects in the light of the teaching of geometry which emphasizes particular kinds of difficulty faced by teachers. School geometry is rich in activities but it is often not clear what their purpose is, how they fit into a progression of development of mathematical thinking or why certain ones might be selected over others. Tessellations provide a useful example. It is possible to make stories about why tiling patterns are widespread in mathematics lessons.

For example, that working on them helps pupils learn the properties of shapes that make them fit without gaps or deepens their aesthetic appreciation or even that it is included in schemes and textbooks merely because it is currently fashionable. None of these reasons is perhaps convincing on its own and even together they do not give much help in seeing what aspects might be subsequently developed. Even when a teacher decides that tiling patterns *are* an important vehicle for developing their pupils' geometric thinking, they are faced with dozens of tasks to choose from. Tessellations can be created by:

- fitting tiles together (but which tiles? regular polygons? the asymmetric DIME tiles? pentominoes?);
- drawing the shapes on plain, grid or dotted paper;
- creating Islamic patterns;
- overlaying transparent shapes;
- Escher designs;
- using computer software that creates tilings;
- weaving strips ... and many more.

A teacher's choice will be limited by practical constraints, for example having no access to a computer or certain types of tiles not being available, but there will still be many possibilities open. Some selection may be made on the basis of specific mathematical activities which the teacher intends to encourage, for example the accurate use of geometrical instruments, but that will still leave a choice of tasks. In this chapter, we are concerned to examine the bases that teachers have for making their choices.

We look at the tasks that teachers give to children in mathematics lessons, at teachers' intentions, at how they attempt to plan for learning and how they take up opportunities in a lesson to encourage learning. As before, we examine the beliefs and thinking of teachers – in this case, those beliefs which they use to structure their work in the classroom and to plan for their contacts with children. We look more closely at what lies behind planning and teaching mathematics lessons, at giving children activities to do and helping them gain experiences with which to progress through the curriculum.

The nature of classroom events

It is easy to take for granted the structures of lessons. Consider the vocabulary of the things that teachers present to children – lessons, tasks, activities, experiences. By its very familiarity it conceals assumptions that we need to make explicit. In this section we look at these words more closely and especially at the nature of children's activity and the shifting flow of the classroom.

Lessons, tasks, activities and experiences

The first of our anecdotes was intended to evoke the traditional notion of the 'mathematics lesson', which although less widespread now than in the past, will still resonate for many teachers and children:

> It is construed as an 'event' with a definite beginning, an elaboration and a definite end. It has a fixed time duration. Typically all children will be engaged in the same activities which are planned, initiated and controlled by the teacher. Lessons are pitched at the level of the average child with appropriate modifications for 'faster' and 'slower' ones. Typically, instruction, exposition, 'chalk and talk', boardwork, question and answer, are the principal modes of teaching, together with seatwork, practice, and the individual help of those who 'need help'.
>
> *(Bishop and Goffree, 1986, p. 311)*

A mathematics lesson is more than merely a period of time in which children work at mathematics. All teachers of mathematics have conceptions of what lessons will be like. They bring to their teaching the experiences and expectations concerning mathematics lessons that they encountered as pupils; their teacher training – especially for secondary teachers – will have given much attention to producing lessons. Teachers learn how to structure time, to present tasks and to keep the lesson moving; they learn 'pedagogies' such as the sequence of exposition, explanation and then exercises. Moreover, they learn how to '"lessonise" the curriculum' (Bishop and Goffree, 1986, p. 311), that is, to turn schemes of work or chapters of textbooks into lessons and to produce a series of lessons to cover a particular aspect of the curriculum.

Of course, not all lessons are similar. There are those in which classes use individualized work schemes or work through a textbook at their own pace (we consider such lessons later) and, especially in primary schools, there may be only a few children working on mathematics at a time (although such a group will often either be given something similar to a whole-class lesson or will work on an individual basis). In spite of the obvious differences between primary and secondary classrooms, there are also strong resemblances in the ways in which mathematics lessons are conducted. There have been several analyses of the range of lesson types which are applicable across the ages (see Schools Council, 1976; Brissenden, 1980). Brissenden, for example, sees pupils as being involved in 'a sequence of activities' planned by the teacher; these activities differ in the way the class is organized and in the intended kinds of mathematical learning. He distinguishes three ways of organizing a class: working with the class as a whole, small-group work, children working individually; and three kinds of mathematical learning: concept formation, practice of techniques, applications. This classification results in nine possible lesson types. For example, a common type of lesson will concentrate on learning techniques, first through explanation with the whole class and then through individuals working on exercises.

There are two main difficulties with an analysis which sees a lesson as being divided into separate activities. Firstly, lessons are often either too long or too short to serve as a unit for analysing the structuring that teachers do. A complete activity might be a five-minute mental test, a half-hour exercise or a three-week investigation. The first and last of these do not sit easily with the notion of a lesson as a fixed period of time. Secondly, teachers and others involved in mathematics education talk of an activity rather differently, as these comments indicate:

> Constructions made with bricks, kits or other materials often showed interesting and detailed attention to symmetry. These activities offered a wealth of possibilities for using language …

> Most [6- and 7- year-olds] still needed a lot of first-hand experiences, and activities designed to meet this need were a strong feature of effective teaching programmes.

> … Activities ranged from simply identifying positions on a small grid map of Treasure Island to constructing a model town from blocks and other materials …

> *(HMI, 1989, pp. 30, 31, 38)*

In this usage, the term activities is a synonym for certain kinds of task given to children. Originally, the word perhaps referred to tasks in which children, rather than sitting listening or watching, learned by being active: it is now often wider in scope. In his analysis of lessons, Brissenden calls giving children an exercise to complete 'an activity', and the word is often extended to cover an *idea* for a lesson which will result in some pupil activity, for example teacher notes or a workcard. We examine the notion of activity more fully in the next section, and we find it helpful to make a distinction between the terms *task* and *activity*. The task is something set by the teacher, the activity is the learner's. Of course, the purpose in setting a task is to get pupils to engage in particular activities, but the teacher cannot ensure that these activities will take place, as the treasure hunt anecdote indicates. Although the word task often has overtones of something external, perhaps onerous, and with a narrower focus than activity, we use it in a neutral sense: tasks are set by the teacher but result in the learner's activity.* We find that using this distinction helps to clarify the actions of the teacher.

Experiences are also often spoken of as if they could be given to children: 'I need to give her more experience of comparing lengths'. Rather, the teacher can give a task which will result in activity intended to help the child gain experience in comparing lengths. The activity will be that of the child and her experiences will arise from the nature of that activity. Such experiences will, it is hoped, include those intended by the teacher, but there will be many others which depend on the nature of the child's activity. Although experiences appear to be transient, we can neither will them into being nor simply finish with them as we can with an activity:

> Just as no one lives or dies to himself, so no experience lives or dies to itself. Wholly independent of desire or intent every experience lives on in further experiences

> *(Dewey, 1938).*

---

* Teachers who use schemes extensively do not set the tasks themselves, but are, of course, giving children tasks devised by others. Although the discussion that follows is given in terms of tasks set by teachers, it applies just as much – if not more so – to tasks within schemes.

Activity theory

What is activity? A simple answer might be 'the result of any task that involves children in doing something'. But, as usual, things are not so straightforward. Tasks which result in a child's activity might be as various as:

- making a plan of the playground;
- constructing a circle;
- completing an exercise of naming angles;
- devising and carrying out a Logo project.

With such a range of possibilities, activity becomes much too general a term to be helpful in analysing teachers' thinking. A theory of activity has been developed by some Soviet educational psychologists which, although conceived in very general terms, throws light on what we call activities in the classroom.* To give a focus to the discussion, we return to the treasure hunt anecdote at the beginning of this chapter. What has gone wrong here? Leont'ev, Galperin and Davydov suggest that the *actions* carried out by children need to be distinguished from their *activity*. A specific action may be used in many different activities. Darren's actions – entering suitable coordinates, moving on when he has found the treasure – are the correct ones; but his activity is not the one envisaged by the teacher. The crucial difference is that his motive for his activity – what he is trying to do with the task set – is not the same as the teacher's. We do not, of course, know Darren's motive – it is, perhaps, to find the treasure and thus complete the task. Although Darren is carrying out suitable actions, he is engaged in an inappropriate activity. At worst he is simply trying to get the task finished; at best, he misunderstands what it is he is supposed to gain from undertaking the task.

Leont'ev sees activity as 'a process which is always initiated by and interpreted in the perspective of a motive' (Christiansen and Walther, 1986, p. 255) and the most important differences between activities are due to differences in the motives of the person carrying them out. People form images or representations in their minds about things they want to do, and these images in turn serve as a way of helping them see themselves in relation to the world: that is, they acquire motives. Activity results when a person acts to fulfil a motive, this will give rise to goals which the person attempts to reach by performing actions. An *action* is a goal-directed process caused by the motive of the activity. Darren's motive may be – we cannot be sure – to complete the task which he knows he can do by finding the treasure. This then becomes the goal of his actions. To reach this goal he has no need to devise strategies or be systematic and so his activity is different from that conceived by the teacher.

This idea of activity as 'actions with a motive' is important for educational activities. In children's normal, everyday activity they initiate activity to satisfy their own motives, but educational activity is initiated in response to the teacher's task. When teachers set a task, *their* intention is that the task promotes certain kinds of learning, but the child's motive will depend on how the task is seen. As Christiansen and Walther say,

---

* This work has been developed by Leont'ev, Galperin, and Davydov, taking ideas from Vygotsky. We draw on the account by Christiansen and Walther (1986) pp. 254 ff.

> ... even when students work on assigned tasks supported by carefully
> established educational contexts and by corresponding teacher-ac-
> tions, learning as intended does not follow automatically from their
> activity on the tasks.

(Christiansen and Walther, 1986, p. 262)

Activity can fail to produce the intended learning in all sorts of ways. The
children's primary motive may simply be to do the task set by the teacher, rather
than being concerned to learn something. Even when they see their activity in
terms of trying to learn, they may have considerable difficulties in understanding
what it is the teacher wants them to learn. This difference between how the
children and the teacher see the task is the major problem in trying to devise
learning activities. For example, when children become absorbed by the task set
by the teacher, they often become absorbed in the *doing* of the task – carefully
drawing lines, colouring shapes, cutting. Their attention is on the doing, they are
being active, they are engaging in activity, but they may not be learning what is
intended. Of course, they are likely to be learning *something*. Since a teacher cannot
ever know what is being learned by a child doing an activity, some highly
valuable learning, for example developing skills in cutting or holding a ruler or
being able to make an accurate copy of another drawing, may be taking place.

It is evident that there is nothing inherent in a task or its associated activity that
will result in the intended learning. What is crucial is the child's perception of the
task and the activity. Activity theory suggests that there are three ways in which
people perceive and control their own activity. First, by their 'internal maps of the
world – their structure of already acquired knowledge, concepts, self-under-
standing, systems of values and norms, positions, viewpoints'. Second, by their
internal representation of what it is they wish to do; and third, by using feedback
'to compare data collected in the environment with answers established by means
of [their] internal maps' (Christiansen and Walther, 1986, p. 257). Each of these
will cause modifications in the pupil's view of the task and probably to the task
itself. This aspect is taken up in the next section.

Christiansen and Walther suggest that the key aspects which affect the child's
activity in class are:

> ... the individual's interest in the task, his motivation for acting, his
> attitudes towards the teacher and the school, his conceptions of
> learning and of mathematics ... and ... whether he *reflects* on his actions
> and on his own learning.

(Christiansen and Walther, 1986, p. 262)

In the treasure hunt example, another child may realize that a requirement of the
task is that she should be systematic in searching for the treasure. If she goes no
further than seeing it as a task with those conditions she may still fail to learn what
the teacher considers important. The teacher might intend that the activity should
help the child learn how to search systematically or to develop a strategy, as well
as giving practice in labelling the coordinates of grid points. The thrust of the
remarks above is that *reflection* by the child on what she has done and learned is
essential. If the child's motive remains to complete the task, the activity will not
be the learning activity intended by the teacher.

The emphasis on 'reflection' might seem surprising. It could be argued that most of us have learned a very great deal without having reflection built in to what we were working on. We want to distinguish between those parts of lessons in which the teacher explicitly aims to get children reflecting on what they have done and the reflecting which goes on during a task. The latter occurs whenever a pupil is trying to see how something is done or is making comparisons between what is achieved and what was intended, gaining feedback and using this to modify what is being done. Children will carry out such actions without prompting in all kinds of circumstances, and many of them do so while working in mathematics lessons. This kind of informal reflection is a key to much learning and, as we discuss below, it is possible for teachers to devise tasks that are likely to promote such thinking.

The more overt forms of reflection are usually controlled by teachers and often taken over by them. In the treasure hunt example, it is the teacher who sees that Darren is failing to carry out the right activity and she will very likely attempt to change this, perhaps by making the conditions of the task more explicit. That is, she draws attention to her learning objective for the task to try to influence Darren's motives.

Thus, the teacher's attempts to engage pupils in their own learning is frequently at odds with the pupil's activity. The teacher proposes an investigation into, say, tessellations of pentominoes, feeling that this is a task likely to be of interest to the pupil. The pupils may well become interested in this problem and be able accept that they are trying to learn something by working on it. But there is a further issue: how can the pupils know just what it is that they are intended to learn before they have worked on the task? Does it matter whether the pupils know this?

Negotiating in the classroom

This discussion of activity theory underlines the crucial importance of the pupil's motives in response to a task from the teacher. How does the teacher enable the learner to approach the task with appropriate motives? In some sense, there has to be a rapprochement between the learner and the teacher. Hitherto, we have treated the task, the activity and the mathematics to be learned as if they were fixed. This is far from the case: the teacher's attempt to help the pupil acquire appropriate motives involves modifying each of these – usually in the flow of the lesson.

At one extreme, the teacher may attempt to base the tasks primarily on activity stemming from the individual's personal needs and interests. As a general principle this is misguided because it will not always be possible to incorporate all of the desired aspects of mathematics in such activity but also because 'learning to learn in school consists also in acceptance of tasks set by the teacher and acceptance of the necessity of paying attention to such assignments' (Christiansen and Walther, 1986, pp. 264–5).

This sounds rather as though a learner needs to subjugate themselves to the teacher's power, and indeed some degree of subordination is inevitable because the teacher is both an adult and more expert than the children. But the outcome is far from being one sided. What actually happens is that pupils and teachers constantly negotiate and renegotiate the meaning of ideas, tasks and activities in the classroom. This may involve surrender on the part of the pupil ('No, that is wrong. This is what you have to do.') but more often it involves mutual redefining. Delamont in her study of classroom interactions claims that 'the pupil's first strategy is to provide "correct" – that is, acceptable to the teacher – answers. To do this, they must concentrate on the teacher enough to discover what the right answers are, or are likely to be' (1976, p. 101).

This strategy extends beyond simply giving correct answers to carrying out the 'correct' actions. If the pupils do not seem able to do the correct thing, teachers adapt the task to what they see as the needs of their pupils, perhaps simplifying it by providing extra explanations or clues or splitting it into smaller parts. In interactions there is usually a frequent to and fro of negotiation between the teacher and pupil, each developing their strategies. The pupils are trying to discover what it is they have to do to satisfy the teacher; the teacher is trying to modify the task suitably while keeping the original aim in mind. The strategies adopted depend intimately on the interactions between teachers and pupils 'because they develop in interpersonal and social contexts where the cues, signals, demands and feedback are given … personally' (Bishop and Goffree, 1986, p. 345).

Because Darren was carrying out a different activity from the one intended, his teacher had to find a way of getting him to carry it out more appropriately. This is not straightforward and, as often happens to a hard-pressed teacher, she might decide to modify her intention for the task so that a sufficient outcome would be Darren learning the right way to describe coordinates. Such simplification of the task is a very common form of negotiation in the classroom, sometimes brought on by a pupil persistently asking for help and perhaps initiating the funnel effect described in Chapter 2. On the other hand, teachers frequently exercise considerable ingenuity in enabling pupils to return to a task after it has been misunderstood or treated inappropriately. More importantly, the negotiation allows the teacher to adapt a task to make it more suitable to the class or individuals – by taking up interests revealed by discussion, by seizing opportunities to make the task more demanding or to extend it.

The other principal kind of negotiation involves negotiating the meaning of the mathematics being worked upon. This might seem surprising as mathematics is thought of as a fixed body of knowledge. But although teachers might have such knowledge their pupils do not and it cannot be transmitted directly.

> A new idea is meaningful to the extent to which individuals can connect it with their existing knowledge. Mathematical ideas will connect in some way with other mathematical ideas but also with other aspects of personal knowledge. In particular, the teacher has one set of meanings and connections while the learners will have theirs – again, unique to each individual.

> *(Bishop and Goffree, 1986, p. 346)*

Teachers regularly use their authority to impose mathematical meaning on pupils. Although this might be done in a direct way, frequently it occurs when the teacher evaluates the pupil's response in a questioning session as discussed in

Chapter 2. By reading the teacher's acceptance or rejection of a response, the pupil builds up a picture of what the mathematics means. In such circumstances, the teacher is using a rather less overt form of coercion, which stems from the teacher's evaluation of the pupil's response as right or wrong. But there is also a real sense in which it is possible for the meaning of the mathematics to be negotiated through discussions in which the pupils' understandings are exposed to scrutiny, as described in Chapter 2.

The analysis of activity underlines the need for children to be interested in the task in such a way that they will be motivated to appropriate activity. This might seem obvious, but 'interest 'and 'motivation' have been much abused words. John Dewey, in a short book written in 1913, examined types of interest and the connection with motivation and effort. He castigated both 'making things interesting' and any suggestion that motivation is related to a narrow sense of the usefulness of a task, and claimed that genuine interest happens when pupils need to be able to do something in order to continue with a self-initiated activity.

> Genuine interest ... simply means that a person has identified himself with, or has found himself in, a certain course of action. Consequently he is identified with whatever objects and forms of skill are involved in the successful prosecution of that course.
>
> *(Dewey, 1913)*

There is a clear connection to activity theory here. Children need to wish to learn whatever it is that a learning activity is intended to promote. Dewey suggests that wishing to put effort into an activity is the outcome of such genuine interest. In order to promote such genuine interest, the Soviet psychologists suggest that teachers need to attend to the three ways in which children control their activity: what internal maps the children have, how they think about the purposes of a task and how they can gain feedback in their activity.

Schemes

Our earlier accounts of lessons and activities were only partial. The depiction of teachers choosing tasks and presenting a lesson is often far from the practice of many teachers – those who rely heavily on a commercial scheme. In a survey of primary schools in England and Wales, HMI found that:

> In many schools [published] materials were the principal or sole determinant of the children's programme of work. Only in the minority of classes did teachers use published materials selectively as part of a broader strategy of teaching ...
>
> *(HMI, 1989, p. 10)*

The range of materials covered by the word 'scheme' ranges from 'individualized' systems of workcards and booklets, via an organized collection of very varied resources, to a yearly series of textbooks. Equally, the ways in which teachers use a scheme can vary widely. However, all schemes do have characteristics in common. Not only does the scheme help teachers organize the mathematics curriculum but it also organizes the work of the classroom. There is no apparent need for teachers to choose tasks or to decide how to present them. The tasks are chosen by the devisers of the scheme and presented in the form of booklets or workcards. The effect of using a scheme is to make some aspects of classroom life easier and others more difficult.

When pupils work from the cards or booklets or textbooks independently of the teacher, the teacher has different kinds of interactions from those in a 'mathematics lesson'. She spends much less time instigating activity or posing questions, and more time answering questions, giving help, checking and marking. Although these are less interesting activities for the teacher, the compensatory benefits of using one are seen to be that schemes:

- provide a framework for establishing continuity of experience within the school;

- possess a rich variety of ideas for treating concepts and processes;

- help keep children busy – and solve the management problems created by the attempt to provide a diversified curriculum;

- confer status on the definition of the contents of a school's mathematics curriculum as they have been designed by experts in mathematics education.

(Adapted from Desforges and Cockburn, 1987, pp. 46, 47)

These benefits are considerable, but schemes have been heavily criticized for their effect on the mathematics curriculum. In Desforges and Cockburn, some primary teachers commented:

> I would never have bought a scheme like this in a million years ... It's not that it is bad, it's uninteresting ... Schemes make such heavy weather of things. They seem to batten hatches down in case something goes adrift.

> Schemes save teachers from thinking. ... They are insensitive to the difference between children.

> Schemes are dangerous. ... they absolve you from decisions about appropriate work and sequence.

(Desforges and Cockburn, 1987, p. 42)

In another project a secondary teacher said:

> As work is self-marked only questions with a single answer are asked ... but some of the cards do say 'What do you notice?' Pupils quickly learn that there is AN answer to this too and either look up answers or ask a teacher, who provides the words. Responses not in the exact form of words in the answer sheets are marked wrong by pupils. Any teacher intervention in this process, with positive encouragement to speculate, is viewed with suspicion. Authority rests with the answer sheets!

(DES, 1987, p. 49)

In an overview of primary mathematics, the HMI of England and Wales, referring to published schemes, observed that:

> In many classes the content and pace of work in mathematics are determined by the sequence within a series of textbooks or workcards. There has been a consequent increase in two problems ... associated with the over-use of assignment cards: insufficient time given to direct teaching and to discussion, and too much practice of skills that have already been mastered.
>
> *(HMI, 1989, p. 13)*

Schemes provide a huge amount of security. The teacher does not have to do either large-scale planning (where the curriculum has to be organized into separate topics) or small-scale (thinking how to present a particular task). This might seem ideal for the teacher but the drawbacks that have been indicated are, however, endemic to using schemes. Using our previous analysis of activity we can interpret what happens in classes which learn mathematics largely through the use of a scheme.

Firstly, it is difficult for the teacher to know what are the intended learning outcomes. Once the teacher is familiar with a scheme and operating it comfortably, she does not need to prepare the tasks and so she does not consider what are the intended learning outcomes of each booklet or card. It then becomes much more difficult to address the problem of whether the pupils' activities as a result of the task in the booklets are those intended or are some redefined version. This mechanizing effect is pervasive: the longer a scheme is in use, the more it is likely to occur. The same effect is likely to occur eventually even when the scheme is 'home grown' but then it is easier for teachers to recover control because replacing or renewing such a scheme is not an all-or-nothing process as it would be with a commercial one.

Secondly, a predominant motive for the activity of many pupils becomes 'to get through the cards'. This will be done by completing each card as quickly as possible, which is likely to involve the pupils in re-defining the task so that it becomes as simple as possible.

Thirdly, it is more difficult to create genuine interest in the pupils. This happens because the purposes of the activity are not so readily accessible to the child – they have only the workcard to help them in this rather than the full resources of the teacher as they would frequently have in other kinds of mathematics lessons.

Fourthly, because pupils have to be able to work through the cards unaided, the mathematical ideas, the types of task and the language of cards need to be such that they will not give difficulty to an isolated pupil. This always results in simplification, often drastically altering the mathematical demands of a task. Tasks in which meaning is developed as the task proceeds are difficult to incorporate into schemes because whatever appears written seems to be determined and fixed. The kinds of negotiation that a teacher can make when introducing or extending a task – giving tentative suggestions and qualifications – are absent with consequent losses for both the teacher and children. The teacher loses the satisfactions of explaining and of interacting; the children (although they are unlikely to know this) lose opportunities to engage with mathematics in ways that will increase their learning. Tasks tend to become formalized or made into a series of routines. At their least demanding this can become filling in blanks on a sheet. This effect was evoked by Judy Morgan in connection with a Scottish secondary scheme.

> As he faces his sheet ... the child ... has little time to read the instructions in a way which we would describe as 'carefully'. He looks at the first half of the sheet and searches for clues on how to fill in the blanks. He looks and finds a visual pattern, he checks his pattern with another example; if they fit, he proceeds and fills in as many spaces as he can. He barely notices the carefully underlined or capitalised phrases which remind him succinctly of what he is doing.

> *(Morgan, 1977, p. 54)*

Designing tasks

In this section we look at the tasks that teachers give to pupils: at the planning that the teacher undertakes and the ways in which this is modified in the classroom and at what characteristics tasks might need if they are to promote learning.

On planning

Many experienced mathematics teachers frequently seem to undertake almost no explicit planning for a lesson. This impression of lack of preparation is of course wildly misleading. Such teachers have books and other resources and schemes of work that are familiar to them and are supported by the structure of the school and day. They also bring to a classroom their previous experience of how to organize a lesson, how to select and adapt materials and resources as the flow of the lesson proceeds, how to adapt to the needs of pupils, how to devise a task for a particular purpose, how to make use of, control or neutralize unexpected events. All of this gives them the confidence to 'fly by the seat of their pants'; they have a host of ways of thinking about their encounters with children that they can draw upon. When a teacher uses a scheme, there are even more resources and precedents to draw upon.

In the course of planning, teachers habitually think about mathematical content (Chapter 1); classroom interactions (Chapter 2); and the task and activity (as described in the earlier sections of this chapter). The more experienced a teacher is, the more automated such planning becomes – a teacher does not have to go through the whole process but can take many things for granted. This, of course, enables them to do other things with their time including thinking about how to vary their teaching. But it has costs in pushing the teacher's assumptions further into the background, making them less easy to change.

We can contrast two instances of planning: a teacher regularly using a familiar textbook decides to use a particular chapter and to use it in a straightforward way, such a decision may only take a few moments reflection – she may know that children usually have problems with this chapter but is confident that she can modify it in the class as the lesson proceeds. On another occasion she wishes to teach in an unfamiliar way and with unfamiliar materials. This time she rehearses in her mind the general strategies she will employ during the lesson: starting the activity, how to keep it going and adds particular details of things she will stress and perhaps even comments she will make.

When teachers know what they want to do in class, there is little to plan. It has been said that 'planning is what you do when you are not sure what you can do'. Experienced teachers can visualize themselves into a lesson and imagine what is going to happen – indeed mental imagery is integral to planning. If teachers do not know what they want to do, they attempt to picture the possibilities.

When dealing with the unfamiliar, planning offers security: a feeling of having it all worked out in advance, so that you can cope with whatever happens. This is not always desirable, however, and there are often occasions when such detailed planning is counter-productive. If the teacher is going to present an open-ended investigation, she may spend a long time doing her own working from the starting-point before taking it into the class. She may then find that her aim of getting the class to explore freely is more difficult to achieve. Because her own investigations are so much in her mind she responds more readily to suggestions that indicate directions which were productive for her, and less so to ones she has not herself explored or feels might lead to a dead end.

Usually, teachers do not plan out all the details in advance but they do plan and devise materials with a mixture of general strategy and particular parts planned in great detail. But one aspect that regularly goes unexamined is the overall structuring of a task and this is what we turn to now.

Classroom tasks for promoting learning

In the first of our anecdotes, the teacher explained some types of triangles and let the pupils work through a textbook page. This is a widely-used instance of what might be called an exposition-exercise structure. The tasks in the other two anecdotes draw upon other structures: playing a game and being presented with a situation to explore. All of these have behind them ideas about what kinds of pupils' activity will result in learning. They all involve the pupils in doing something but differ in whether or what pupils are told, the degree of assistance and the amount of interaction with others. We now look at what are the desirable components of pupils' activity if they are to learn and then at some ways in which tasks are structured.

The first essential for learning mathematics is *doing things* – in the sense of being engaged in an activity, being embroiled in some task. Through manipulating physical objects or mental images or written symbols, one comes to see patterns and relationships, to form concepts, to make connections. Doing by itself is not sufficient, however: how many things there are that people do everyday and yet fail to learn from! When attention is totally absorbed, there is none left for constructing some story, some explanation or account of what one is doing in order to seek similarities and differences with other situations; in other words in order to put it into context and make it accessible in the future. With engagement is needed periods of distancing, of reflecting upon the doing, so that something is learned.

Seeing patterns and connections is also essential. In one sense, it is what learning mathematics is really about. Seeing patterns and connections is often enhanced from that most mathematical of activities: predicting (making conjectures about) what will happen, then testing the prediction and modifying the conjecture on the basis of experience. Conjectures can sometimes be tested in the physical world which is why mathematics and science cannot be easily separated in the infant school. As mathematical thinking develops, they are more often tested in the mathematical world of mental images, ideas and symbols. Hence the necessity for becoming comfortable with symbolic formulations of patterns and generalities.

But seeing does not just happen. One way in which seeing patterns and connections can be stimulated is through talking about what one is doing and seeing. Saying things to others, explaining half-formed ideas and listening to what others say make important contributions to clarifying and organizing one's thinking. They assist people to reformulate ideas in their own terms and to reconstruct experiences they have had.

Doing, seeing and talking are still not enough for learning from mathematical experience for they are ephemeral activities. Within a short space of time, ideas which seemed clear and obvious can disappear from the mind. Mathematical thinking particularly benefits from written records of one's thinking because it develops from the manipulation of physical objects to the manipulation of mental objects and of symbols written on the page.

Recording thoughts in words, in pictures, in symbols, in calculator key-sequences and in computer programs not only gives teachers access to the qualities of pupils' thinking but actually advances the pupils' mathematical thinking. The words, pictures and symbols come to represent objects which are themselves manipulated in further pattern spotting, in expressing generalities, in formulating further conjectures and justifications.

Types of tasks

Even when tasks include the actions of doing, seeing, talking and recording there is still the problem of how teachers can best encourage pupils to adopt appropriate motives for their activity. For example, how can a teacher get pupils to concentrate on developing generalizations rather than on getting the right pattern? We need to look for types of task which embody the essential requirements for learning to take place as well as ensuring that pupils will be able to reflect on their learning. Although there are no infallible methods of ensuring that the focus of pupils' work becomes their own learning, teachers have devised kinds of tasks which are more likely to confront learners with the need to be aware of their learning.* Some of these are:

---

*   In what follows we have drawn on a series of articles on 'Diagnostic teaching' by
    Alan Bell and others in *Mathematics Teaching*.

- Games in which pupils are called upon to see and express certain patterns or connections. The pleasure pupils get from playing games serves to keep them in situations where the use of technical language to describe what they are doing or seeing enables them to become confident in the use of the language. Words are no longer memorized incantations but actually express their thoughts.

- Challenges can be offered so that pupils' attention is focused on discovery, but in the process they are called upon to exercise particular skills sufficiently to become automated. A task originally devised by the Madison Project asks children to fit numbers into quadratic expressions such as:

$$(\square \times \square) - (5 \times \square) + 6 = 0$$

and see if they get a true statement. Some numbers work and others do not. Are there any rules for deciding which numbers give the true statements?

The children are set the task of looking for such rules and this may be how they view what they are engaged upon. But the teacher's intention for the lesson is to get them to practise substituting values for a variable and to gain an awareness of what a variable is. The actual rules themselves are seen as unimportant for future mathematical learning.

The whole point of automating a skill is to release attention away from the doing and into directing the skill to some greater goal. Consequently in order to assist pupils to automate a skill, their attention needs to be directed away from the doing. Sets of routine exercises rarely have this effect because attention is directed towards the very skill or technique to be automated.

- Another type of task involves situations which appear to involve contradictions, paradoxes or surprises. With these, pupils find themselves wanting to sort out what is happening, to resolve differences of opinion or conflicting explanations, to find some way to account for what is happening. Pupils are called upon to explain things for each other and to locate differences and agreements in their explanations. The areas of triangles anecdote is an instance of this kind of task.

In general, these kinds of task aim to make explicit to learners their own difficulties. They frequently rely on discussion to do this and some of the techniques used are as follows.

- Pupils devise their own questions and give these to others not only for them to do but also to discuss whether they are easy, hard, similar to one another, and so on.

- Children are encouraged to tell stories about a problem – especially if it is lacking in a context.

- 'Conflict-discussion lessons' in which the problems are ones about which pupils were likely to disagree on methods or results and yet be especially convinced of their own correctness. Conflicts are thus built in and are resolved by groups of pupils discussing their different results.

- Building reflection into the end of a task where the children are asked to present verbal or written accounts of what they have learned.

Tasks like these should include the essential aspects required for learning (as outlined above). They should also help pupils' awareness of the purpose of the task, so that it can be approached with an appropriate motivation. One problem for teachers in trying to use the tasks is that the activity they produce often runs counter to teachers' views on the proper way to encourage learning. Thus in many of the tasks, explaining the mathematics involved – as distinct from clarifying the task – is likely to defeat the purpose of the task. Bell comments:

> For many teachers it is difficult to organise discussion so that misconceptions are brought to the surface. In fact, some of the teachers organised their pupils by groups, but then spent their time touring the class helping the groups in the usual way, without any particular emphasis on exposing and discussing the misconceptions.
>
> *(Bell, 1987b, p. 53)*

Creating tasks in the classroom

In the classroom, teachers use pre-planned materials and ideas but they also take advantage of unanticipated events. At its most mundane, such an event might be a child failing to understand an explanation of how to draw a line parallel to another; at the other extreme, the teacher may jettison a prepared lesson in favour of some inspiration arising from an unexpected intervention by a child. In a junior school, a child brought in two sheep skulls which the teacher was able to use to look at work on comparative sizes of animals. Such teacher reactions involve both letting go and holding on to control. Teachers may have predispositions which limit their possible deviations from their planning.

> ... some teachers rely heavily on established routines, conventional subject matter and stereotyped patterns of teacher–pupil relations, while others are constantly at work giving form to the subject matter taught and to the activities of the classroom.
>
> *(Elbaz, 1983, p. 90)*

When teachers spontaneously react to an unexpected event, one dimension is that of change or novelty.

> The notion of spontaneity ... involves two opposing factors. The first is the ability to release control, to receive stimuli from outside, and to respond to a situation or to a person. ... The other factor is the ability to control the spontaneous event, to use the special energies which it releases to move learners in a direction intended by the teacher.
>
> *(Elbaz, 1983, p. 91)*

Such openness to outside events runs against the design principle on which much advice on curriculum planning rests. In the design procedure, aims and outcomes are decided, the means to achieve them determined and then the process is put into operation. The key feature of the procedure is that you have to know what you want to do in advance of doing it. This is inadequate for teaching, not simply because it does not allow for the spontaneous happening, but also because:

> … a description of a task, an analysis of its potentials, and advice to the teacher about possible guidance … which he might exert in his class, are steps which are *external* to the task, to the teacher and the learner, and to their activity and interaction in the teaching/learning process.

(Christiansen and Walther, 1987, p. 264)

In other words, teachers always have to operate in the classroom with the moment-to-moment reality of their pupils which will always have aspects above and beyond any planning. A more suitable organizing principle than designing has been called 'eolithism':

> An eolith is literally a piece of junk remaining from the stone age, often enough rescued from some ancient buried garbage heap. … The important matter … is that eoliths *were picked* up, already *accidentally* adapted to some end and, more importantly, *strongly* suggestive of the end. …

> The fashioner of eoliths … must have a continually open mind about materials, and he must be very adaptable in the matter of ends, of what he wants.

(Hawkins, 1974, pp. 21, 22)

In an eolithic mode, a teacher uses what is to hand in the course of a lesson, seeing possible uses for what is around – seizing the moment when an opportunity arises. An infant school visit to the park might generate activity on the motions of swings or making shapes with flowers or the steepness of slopes or a dozen other geometrical activities. Of course the teacher has to be prepared – prepared in that they will recognize the opportunity offered and prepared to use such moments. This eolithic principle does not supplant the design principle – tasks still need to be decided upon – but is complementary to it. In psychoanalysis, Freud, in suggesting a similar procedure, claimed 'the most successful cases are those in which one proceeds as it were without any purpose in view, allows oneself to be taken by surprise by any new turn in them, and always meets them with an open mind free from any suppositions.'

Such a method of working is not so readily available to the teacher using an individualized scheme. There are far fewer eoliths lying around and because the pupils are working by themselves they are much more difficult for the teacher to notice.

One of the problems in using spontaneous events is the potential for leading the teacher into uncharted areas where they feel that their knowledge of the subject matter is shaky. This can be particularly true in investigatory lessons when totally unexpected directions might emerge. Many teachers feel insecure at such a point: they feel the lack of a framework, that the lesson is moving out of their control. Other teachers have the confidence to cope with being adrift, in allowing unexpected lines of enquiry to be followed. For some this confidence partly resides in mathematics. Because they see mathematics as a way of working rather than a body of knowledge, they are not dismayed by their lack of specific knowledge of the outcome. In the words of David Fielker in such a situation, 'I knew the mathematics would see me through'.

What seems to matter in such circumstances is the development of teacher judgement. Such judgements will always be based on the teacher's experience and will be highly dependent on the day-to-day context in which the teacher makes decisions.

> ... for every behaviour you can identify as characteristic of a teacher of mathematics someone else will produce the opposite. ...
>
> You will be able to recall things describable as opposite which you have done in apparently similar circumstances. For instance, the judgement that allows you to stop a child giving an answer will be used on another occasion to encourage a child to give an answer; or the decision to allow a child to choose his own method will be countered on another occasion by a decision not to.
>
> *(Brookes, 1978, p. 6)*

Turning the curriculum into tasks

In this final section, we look at issues concerned with the ways in which the broad sweep of the mathematics curriculum gets turned into tasks in the classroom. There are two aspects here: the idea of progression in the tasks that teachers give and the mathematical purposes of tasks.

Progression in mathematical tasks

As children get older, we would expect the tasks given to them to change: they will be able to tackle more complex and difficult tasks and show more insight. They will not only build on what has been learned but extend it in some way. Progression is not concerned simply with work getting harder or more complicated – it implies a development, a deepening of awareness and an enlargement of the range of contexts that can be dealt with. In geometry, there is a problem in deciding which geometrical notions to attend to – be it the idea of symmetry, of naming shapes, of imagery or of geometrical contexts. If we contrast geometry with number, it is easy to see what the problem is. Numbers get bigger, more complicated techniques are needed to calculate with them, new operations are introduced, the notion of number is extended from whole numbers to fractions and decimals to negative numbers and beyond. This structure both provides the content and is the line of development in teaching number. There is little that is analogous to this in dealing with polygons or tessellations or symmetry.

These difficulties can be illustrated by looking at the development of symmetry. Many schemes have only a few standard tasks such as producing ink-blots, folding a piece of paper in two and cutting out a shape, identifying symmetries on drawings of objects. These occur in school-books for infants and those for twelve-year-olds, with no sense of deepening insight or of what is being aimed at. The national curriculum for England and Wales has several statements on symmetry in the programmes of study for attainment target 4: shape and space:

- recognising the (reflective) symmetry in a variety of shapes in 2 and 3 dimensions (Level 3)
- recognising rotational symmetry (Level 4)
- identifing the symmetries of various shapes (Level 5)
- reflecting simple shapes in a mirror line (Level 6)

(DES/WO, 1991)

The intention is that these represent a progression in symmetry, but it is easy to find examples of, say, recognizing 3-D symmetry that children find more difficult than drawing a simple reflection. Again there is no notion here of what it means for a person to develop their idea of symmetry.

Symmetry is a relatively easy notion compared with others that we might wish to develop in the geometry curriculum. It is much harder, for example, to decide what might count as development in pupils' ability to control and use their imagery.

The national curriculum list above points to the inadequacy of any list, with whatever authority it has behind it. Those who compile a list always have images in their mind of connections between the items which reflect the purposes for including them. A list always has an implied structure. 'Reflecting simple shapes in a mirror line' comes with assumptions about whether these shapes are drawn on paper, whether the paper has grid squares or dots on it, what are thought to be simple shapes.

Another person encountering the list always brings to it their structures. Simply taking a list as such is likely to produce a series of disconnected items – and result in mathematics as a smorgasbord. There are innumerable enjoyable geometric tasks but they are not enough on their own and teachers need principles on how to choose from them. These organizing principles are elusive; there are stories that we are helping children develop their geometric awarenesses or their abilities to visualize but such suggestions only ever seem to be part of the whole. It is hard to know even what principles might organize thinking about development.

We need to look at the historical development of the teaching of geometry to understand what the difficulty is. Euclid's *Elements*, which has been the single greatest influence on the study of geometry, has had several profound effects:

- it determined that geometry would be the study of points, lines, circles, planes and so on;
- it asserted the primacy of two dimensions over three dimensions;
- it set up a model for the development of geometry from definitions ('a straight line is the shortest distance between two points'), through axioms to theorems; and established this chain through the notion of proof.

There have been other major influences – the use of coordinates, the idea of symmetry, the concept of transformations – but these have usually been conceived within one or more aspects of the framework set up by Euclid. Until the end of the nineteenth century, the content of geometry courses was that of Euclid, with some additions, and the principal method of teaching and learning geometry was via the sequence outlined in the third point above. As an organizing principle for the teaching of geometry this framework collapsed around the turn of the century. As David Fielker has commented:

> The tragedy of Euclid was that only a small minority of pupils could appreciate the processes of logical deduction in the formality of the context, let alone any overall logical development from a set of axioms; the rest tried to memorise theorems in the hope of obtaining all their examination marks from those [rather than from problems based on the theorems].
>
> *(Fielker, 1983, p. 54)*

There was an initial attempt in this country to replace the Euclidean programme with a three-stage learning process:

- experimentation to establish properties of shapes and figures;
- learning to prove geometric theorems;
- a systematizing stage when the theorems were arranged in a logical sequence.

The first two stages found their way into the curricula of many grammar schools, but the full programme was hardly ever implemented.

In the mathematics teaching reforms in the 1950s and 1960s other content ideas (for example, coordinates, symmetry, transformations) were introduced and incorporating these fragmented any framework for progression even further. Today, there is little more than a collection of disjointed items and this is reflected in the failure of the various national curricula in the United Kingdom to offer a coherent and meaningful organization of the geometrical aspects. As we have suggested earlier, the content aspects of geometry are not sufficient on their own for creating a curriculum: some further organizing principles are needed.

Further attempts have been made to find replacement structures for Euclid, both mathematical and pedagogic. We briefly outline several ways that people have sought to see a development in children's mathematical thinking.

- A development from object → transformation → transformation as object
  An example of this is a treatment of symmetry which starts by isolating the property of symmetry from objects, emphasizing the mirror aspect, and extends the idea to reflection in a mirror line. Whereas at first the symmetry of the object was the concern, now the transformation 'reflection in that particular line' is the focus, and the properties of the reflection as a whole, rather than the effect on particular shapes. This leads to a treatment of reflections in different mirror lines.

- A development from whole → part → part as attribute → attribute as object (due to van Hiele). At first, young children see shapes as wholes but with no evidence of awareness of details. They go on to have some sense of parts which go to make a shape, are able to see some shapes embedded in others, and then to have a growing sense of connections among the parts and that shapes can have properties.

- Another aspect of development is by widening of the range of contexts in which geometry can be recognized. Young children may be able to see squares and triangles in houses and roofs, and this can be deepened by learning to see less obvious examples – parallelograms in derailleur gears, the shapes on a football, the perspective effects of photographs. A subsequent stage in development is to see how the geometrical properties of objects force particular shapes or motions – the effect of undulating land on the lines in a ploughed field, of shadows of railing on steps, of the motions of various types of hinged doors.

These are by no means the only structures that can be used to think of development in geometry. One characteristic they seem to share is that progression involves ideas becoming components of further thinking. The reason that structures of this kind are of concern to teachers is that only by the means of such frameworks can they make other than off-the-cuff choices from the range of tasks or attempt to give a suitable shape to the pupils' activities. Teachers who use schemes extensively have such decisions taken away from them. The curriculum designers have chosen the tasks although, of course, even if they have a well thought-out rationale for including various tasks (as we have seen, not an easy matter), there may be a huge gap between their intentions and those that the teacher can read into the materials of the scheme. There is evidence that teachers who use schemes tend to think of progression in terms of progression through the booklets or workcards rather than in a mathematical or developmental sense.

However, none of the above is sufficiently detailed to construct a curriculum and, more importantly, each one is too partial. Geometry is likely to remain an eclectic enterprise, drawing on many aspects and partially fulfilling many intentions. To focus a curriculum on particular types of shapes or properties is to miss the point of learning geometry: there are no central strands in geometry, no results that are vital in themselves.

The purposes of mathematical tasks and activity

We return finally to the purposes of tasks in mathematics lessons. These purposes are usually wider than simply getting pupils to learn some mathematics. A teacher might intend that a task will challenge the pupils, help them assess their progress, give them practice in a technique. Other purposes might be to quieten the class, to provide time for the teacher to do some other important work, to give the teacher an idea of the attainment of some of the pupils. Although such social motives are always present and often are not easily distinguishable from intentions concerning learning (since they also concern learning and attitudes), we will concentrate here on the learning purposes of activities.

Even where the object is to learn some mathematics, just what aspects of mathematics is not always obvious to a teacher who takes the idea of a task from a teachers' handbook, say, and it is frequently not obvious to the child. The example given earlier of fitting numbers into expressions of the form:

$$(\square \times \square) - (5 \times \square) + 6 = 0$$

is such a task, because what the pupils are being invited to do is not what the teacher intends them to learn.

In connection with geometrical tasks, Dick Tahta (1981) has suggested that a task can been seen as having both inner and outer meanings. The *outer meanings* are the known mathematical results. With tessellation activities these might be the properties of particular quadrilaterals and triangles or sums of angles or, at a rather higher level, the fact that all triangles and quadrilaterals, of whatever shape, will tile the plane. But these do not seem very important matters, certainly not things that will be put to use by pupils. Tahta proposes that the main purpose of such tasks is to engage with the *inner meanings*. In this case, the inner meanings might be the idea of the regularity and infinite repeatability of a tiling pattern or the idea that the whole pattern can be split into blocks that are equivalent and that this can be done in different ways which are in certain senses equivalent, or that it is possible to see many tiling patterns as having the same structure. Meanings that are even more general might be the notion that particular choices of tile will determine particular ways in which they can fit together; or that mathematics is an enterprise where regularities occur in an altogether more systematic way than in other aspects of life.

Returning once again to the treasure hunt anecdote, the outer meanings for Darren's task might be to find the treasure or to develop a strategy for finding the treasure. The inner meanings might concern the characteristics of a good strategy or learning how to be systematic or to obtain a deeper understanding of the idea of a strategy.

The recognition that the surface meanings are not the most important is familiar to teachers of physical education. For the great majority of children, it is not important that they become highly proficient at soccer or netball; the purpose of playing the sport is to help children develop their bodily awareness; to know what it is like to become more skilful physically. Almost any sport will do for these purposes.

These 'hidden meanings' need to be distinguished. In the above example of fitting numbers into boxes, as with the sports one, the ostensible task was more general that the intended one: to some extent, the children are being distracted from what they are meant to learn by being given a more interesting task. The learning may seem to happen incidentally (although the children will have to give attention to it in order to perform their activity). With tessellations the children – and even possibly the teacher – may think that studying the outer meaning is the purpose of the activity and there is a real danger that the task will therefore be rejected as being unimportant. It is such tasks that are most liable to be misconstrued.

There are several implications for these ideas. Firstly, the outer meanings must be attended to as if they mattered. When a person plays a game, it is playing the game that matters not the development of their motor skills; when they are searching for numerical or geometric patterns, the search for the pattern is the driving force. The person has to undergo, to use Coleridge's phrase, a 'willing suspension of disbelief', that is they don't *at that time* question the value of the activity or ask what they are getting from it: their attention is taken by it.

Because of this concentration on the outer meanings, what often happens in school mathematics is that the inner meanings do not emerge: the outer meanings, the surface of the activity, is felt by children to be all that there is. A task on symmetry is seen as getting some paper cut in the right way; pupils may be unclear why they are studying the tilings of pentominoes or the rotations of the hexagon. *Their* activity is to do the ostensible task set by the teacher. The teacher might feel that the exploration of tilings is likely to interest and involve the pupils. But even when the pupils reflect on their learning they frequently do not realize what their activity is helping them to learn. Along with this, they may not see what is important to a task and what peripheral. In the anecdote of the areas of the triangles, the boy thinks he cannot proceed without knowing what a vector is and perhaps thinks that this plays an important role in the investigation. Very little knowledge of vectors was in fact needed (the boy was able to work at the problem when another pupil told him, 'It's the coordinates written on top of one another'). With individualized schemes there are fewer clues about the purposes of a task and missing the inner meanings is likely to be even more prevalent.

A second difficulty is that topics that have been long established in the mathematics curriculum often seem to have no easily separable inner and outer meanings. The study of circumference and area of a circle is in the curriculum in order to learn the relationship between the radius and circumference – perhaps embodied in a formula or spoken language – so that it can be used. Where this apparent fusion of inner and outer meanings occurs the mathematics is taken as being self-evidently important or useful. However, this does not dispose of the issue, because importance or usefulness are not intrinsic properties of some mathematics but are always relative to a particular historical or social context. Many of the disputes about the school mathematics curriculum over the last thirty years have been disputes about the importance or usefulness of various topics. For one person these will be related to everyday use, for another to their place in the structure of mathematical development, for another in requirements for employment of a particular kind – say in industry; for yet another, it will be in developing general thinking processes. (A phrase such as 'the basics' conceals these disagreements.)

In geometry, it is rarely the case that there is this fusion of inner and outer meanings and the inner meanings are often obscure. Much school geometry, especially in primary and lower secondary schools, involves pleasant activities – practical work involving cutting and drawing, doing things with tracing paper or geoboards or linkages; fitting tiles or creating designs. Enjoyable though these activities are it is often difficult to decide what is the point of them and they may be rejected by teachers or children on that account.

Correspondingly, the outer meanings of schemes – including the national curricula in the United Kingdom – seem to concentrate on minor aspects, for example knowing names for shapes, being able to create a mirror reflection, knowing the meaning of 'congruent'. This is the result of a failure to consider the inner/outer distinction. Although we would expect children to acquire these facts and simple skills, they are of little value in themselves. The reason for knowing them is to be able to use them in dealing with and communicating about geometrical aspects of the world.

Some of the inner meanings will be concerned with mathematical content, others with more general issues. The ones mentioned in connection with tessellating perhaps sound a little rarefied, but they are typical of attempts to get beyond the necessary but trivial aspects. Mason suggests that there is one over-arching inner meaning to geometric activities in school: an appreciation that there *are* geometrical facts, that :

> ... some things have to happen, and will always happen, while other things are coincidences, requiring special conditions in order to happen.

> ... what is important about geometry is being aware ... that there are facts, rather than mastery of some particular few facts.

> *(Mason, 1989, pp. 41, 46)*

Summary

In this chapter we have attempted to give an overview of the ways in which teachers can affect the activities that children engage upon in their mathematics class. The focus on geometry has brought several issues to the fore which are perhaps not so prominent in other aspects of mathematics – the issue of progression, the purposes of tasks, indeed the overall intentions for teaching and learning geometry.

The structures that teachers have for thinking about the development of children's mathematics, the meanings that they attach to the purposes of tasks, will affect which tasks they select and how they present these in class, and hence the nature of the activity that their pupils engage in. This will also be true for teachers using schemes, although to a lesser extent, because many of the decisions they might make are pre-empted. However, all learners' activities are determined by their own motives and all teachers need to find ways in which these motives will be directed towards learning the intended mathematics. Some of this can be helped by the design of tasks but much will be done in the interaction with their pupils in the classroom.

Epilogue

It is remarkably difficult to locate one's own attitudes, perceptions and beliefs about mathematics, teaching, and learning. They may emerge in response to events in the classroom, but the very fact of being embroiled in the action means that it is hard to stand back and observe. An external observer sees only the behaviour, without access to the thoughts, images and ideals which comprise the teacher's experience at that moment.

One way to develop an inner teaching-monitor runs parallel to pupils developing an inner mathematical-monitor for themselves. The teacher acts as guide and confidant for the pupil, extending awareness, stretching and challenging, in the sense of Vygotsky. A trusted colleague, with whom it is possible to expose doubts and concerns, can, while observing a lesson, serve to heighten one's own awareness as the lesson is proceeding. In later discussion, descriptions of critical incidents from both points of view can help both parties become aware of aspects of lessons of which previously they have only been vaguely aware. Peter Gates (1989) describes this process which is employed in the Open University course, ME234 *Using Mathematical Thinking*.

A monograph cannot of course provide this service. However, it can, by its own stressing (and consequent ignoring), provide a frame through which to consider one's own experience. The descriptions and suggestions of the chapters will have been successful if they have prompted reflection, generated reaction ('It's not like that for me') and stimulated attempts to expose your own views of mathematics, classroom interactions, and the design of mathematical tasks to promote activity.

A major underlying theme has been the role of language. It is through language that we have suggested some distinctions:

- forms of knowing in mathematics such as symbols, imagery, contexts, techniques and methods, perceptions, intuitions, practical knowledge, and experience;
- forms of telling, asking, and generating discussion which draw upon or activate forms of knowing in mathematics;
- forms of initiating mathematical activity by setting tasks and being aware of the mathematical (and other) thinking processes that tasks are intended to invoke.

It is through language, through expressing themselves to other pupils, to teachers, to parents and later to employers, that pupils come to construct what they know in a form which is accessible to them.

In order to cope with the day-to-day pressure of teaching, it is not possible to consider every action, every move, every reaction. It is essential to automate behaviour. But behaviour once automated becomes habitual and hard to change. The same is true for pupils. Attitudes to mathematics and ways of approaching mathematics in lessons also become habitual and resistant to change. For teacher and for pupil, implicit attitudes, perceptions and beliefs can be both liberating and imprisoning. The same is true of other people's offerings of frames such as those proposed here. The very principle of examining one's attitudes, beliefs and perceptions can be both liberating and stunting: liberating, if it releases fresh approaches and decisions in the moment; stunting, if it sets up a negative spiral of uncertainty and depression because of the inherent impossibility of teaching.

If a proposed distinction acts as a frame to highlight something freshly for a while, then it has acted for the good. If, through contemplating past and present experience, it seems to add meaning, to make sense, then it can become an integral part of one's teaching. If it generates reaction and through that reaction there arises a sharper awareness, which in turn leads to freshness, then all well and good. We see mathematics education not as a logical science which builds inexorably from axioms to truths about teaching and learning but rather as a disciplined enquiry – a personal journey in which awareness develops through action and then fresh action arises through that awareness.

It is perfectly possible to pick up a few slogans, to recite these at every opportunity and to think that one's teaching is developing. Anything which can be used positively also has a negative side to it. Any distinction which helps some people to act freshly can become jargon which inhibits probing more deeply. Any action taken in the classroom which can have a positive effect on pupils can also have a negative side. For example, any form of lesson structure, questioning style or task specification can become habitual and ritualistic, empty of meaning. The only guard against dull habit is variation, balance and continuous inquiry.

Ideals and practice, as we have said, are not always in harmony. Richard Skemp (1979) developed a sophisticated analysis of motivation by observing that goals can attract and 'anti-goals' can repel. Teaching ideals can attract: the individual feels that they are appropriate and fit with experience and so attempts to put them into practice. Teaching ideals can also repel: the individual feels the wish to escape or avoid them and searches around for alternatives. Similarly, a teacher's practice in the classroom can attract some pupils to want to be like that themselves and can repel other pupils who are convinced that they certainly do not want to be that sort of a person.

Actions can be a manifestation of bouncing between several poles, as with the executive-toy pendulum attracted and repelled by magnets. For example, a desire to be merely a resource in the classroom for pupils seeking knowledge, juxtaposed with a national curriculum and a scheme chosen by the school, can generate enormous frustration. Indeed, such a situation is likely to be unstable because, in frustration, teachers are likely to become more directive than they wish in order to gain the confidence of the pupils to achieve necessary short-term goals, while losing contact with long-term aims of independent, autonomous learners.

Through reading and pondering in a conjecturing atmosphere some aspects of the suggestions made here and by acting, at least temporarily, as if they were useful ways of considering mathematics, teaching, and learning, we hope that you have found yourself becoming more aware of your own assumptions and actions which in turn will enable you to notice opportunities to act freshly in the future.

References

AINLEY, J. (1987) 'Telling questions', *Mathematics Teaching*, **118**, pp. 24–6.

BARTOLINI-BUSSI, M. (1990) 'Mathematics knowledge as a collective enterprise' in STEINBRING and SEEGER (eds) *Dialogue between Theory and Practice in Mathematics Education: overcoming the broadcast metaphor*, Germany, Bielefeld.

BELL, A. *et al.* (1978) *Journey into Maths: teacher's guide 1*, London, Blackie, p. 59.

BELL, A. (1986) 'Diagnostic teaching 2: developing conflict-discussion lessons', *Mathematics Teaching*, **116**, pp. 26–9.

BELL, A. (1987) 'Diagnostic teaching 3: provoking discussion', *Mathematics Teaching*, **118**, pp. 21–3.

BELL, A., BREKKE, G. and SWANN, M. (1987a) 'Diagnostic teaching 4: graphical interpretation', *Mathematics Teaching*, **119**, pp. 56–9.

BELL, A., BREKKE, G. and SWANN, M. (1987b) 'Diagnostic teaching 5: graphical interpretation: teaching styles and their effects ', *Mathematics Teaching*, **120**, pp. 50–7.

BELL, A., BREKKE, G. and SWANN, M. (1987c) 'Diagnostic teaching 6: can the same material be used with classes of different ability?', *Mathematics Teaching*, **121**, pp.60–2.

BELL, A. and PURDY, D. (1986) 'Diagnostic teaching', *Mathematics Teaching*, **115**, pp. 39–41.

BERLIN, I. (1981) 'Vico's concept of knowledge' in *Against the Current*, Oxford, Oxford University Press, p. 116.

BERNE, E. (1966) *Games People Play: the psychology of human relationships*, London, Deutsch.

BISHOP, A.J. and GOFFREE, F. (1986) 'Classroom organisation and dynamics' in CHRISTIANSEN, B., HOWSON, A.G. and OTTE, M. (eds) *Perspectives on Mathematics Education*, Dordrecht, Holland, Reidel.

BRISSENDEN, T. (1980) *Mathematics Teaching: theory into practice*, London, Harper & Row.

BRISSENDEN, T. (1988) *Talking About Mathematics: mathematical discussion in primary classrooms*, Oxford, Blackwell.

BROOKES, B. (1978) 'Standards in mathematics teaching', *Mathematics Teaching*, **83**, pp. 2–9.

BROWN, A.C. and FERRARA, R.A. (1985) 'Diagnosing in the zone of proximal development' in WERTSCH, J.V. (ed.) *Culture, Communication and Cognition: Vygotskian perspectives*, Cambridge, Cambridge University Press, pp. 273–305.

BROWN, J.S., COLLINS, A. and DUGUID, P. (1989) 'Situated cognition and the culture of learning', *Educational Researcher*, **18**(1), pp. 32–42.

BRUNER, J. (1986) *Actual Minds, Possible Worlds*, Cambridge, Mass., Harvard University Press.

CHRISTIANSEN, B. and WALTHER, G. (1986) 'Task and activity' in CHRISTIANSEN, B., HOWSON, A.G. and OTTE, M. (eds) *Perspectives on Mathematics Education*, Dordrecht, Holland, Reidel.

DAVIES, B. (1989) *Frogs and Snails and Feminist Tales*, London, Routledge.

DELAMONT, S. (1976) *Interaction in the Classroom*, London, Methuen.

DEPARTMENT OF EDUCATION AND SCIENCE (DES) (1982) *Mathematics Counts*, London, HMSO, (the Cockcroft Report).

DEPARTMENT OF EDUCATION AND SCIENCE (DES) (1987) *Better Mathematics*, report of the Low Attainers in Mathematics Project, London, HMSO.

DEPARTMENT OF EDUCATION AND SCIENCE/WELSH OFFICE (DES/WO) (1991) *Mathematics for Ages 5 to 16* (a consultative document), London, DES/WO.

DESFORGES, C. and COCKBURN, A. (1987) *Understanding the Mathematics Teacher*, Lewes, Falmer.

DEWEY, J. (1913) *Interest and Effort in Education*, 1969 edn reprinted by Cedric Chivers.

DEWEY, J. (1938) *Education and Experience*, 1963 edn reprinted by Collier Books.

DIME PRE-ALGEBRA PROJECT (1984) *Number Patterns 1 – simple mappings*, Stirling, Department of Education, University of Stirling.

EDWARDS, D. and MERCER, N. (1987) *Common Knowledge*, London, Methuen.

ELBAZ, F. (1983) *Teacher Thinking: a study of practical knowledge*, London, Croom Helm.

FIELKER, D. (1983) *Readings in Mathematical Education: removing the shackles of Euclid*, Derby, Association of Teachers of Mathematics, p. 54.

GATES, P. (1989) 'Developing consciousness and pedagogical knowledge through mutual observation' in WOODS, P. (ed.) *Working for Teacher Development*, Dereham, Peter Francis, pp. 11–38.

GATTEGNO, C. (1987) *The Science of Education Part 1: theoretical considerations*, New York, Educational Solutions, p. 60.

HAWKINS, D. (1974) 'Mind and mechanism in education' in *The Informed Vision*, New York, Agathon Press.

HEALY, I., HOYLES, C. and SUTHERLAND, R. (1990) *The Role of Peer Group Discussion in Mathematical Environments*, London, Institute of Education, University of London.

HER MAJESTY'S INSPECTORATE (HMI) (1989) *Aspects of Primary Education: the teaching and learning of mathematics*, London, HMSO.

HOLT, J. (1964) *How Children Fail*, Harmondsworth, Penguin.

HOPKINS, C. (1990) 'A conference tale', *Mathematics Teaching*, **132**, pp. 20–1.

JAWORSKI, B. (1990) '"Scaffolding": a crutch or a support for pupils' sense-making in learning mathematics?' *Proceedings of PME 16*, Mexico.

MASON, J. (1989) 'Geometry: what, why, where and how?', *Mathematics Teaching*, **129**, pp. 41, 46.

MATHEMATICAL ASSOCIATION (1987) *Maths Talk*, Mathematical Association/Stanley Thorne.

MEHAN, H. (1986) '"What time is it Denise?": asking known information questions in classroom discourse' in HAMMERSLEY, M. (ed.) *Case Studies in Classroom Research*, Milton Keynes, Open University Press, pp. 85–103.

MORGAN, J. (1977) *Affective Consequences for the Learning and Teaching of Mathematics of an Individualised Learning Programme*, Stirling, DIME Projects, Department of Education, University of Stirling.

MOVSHOVITS-HADAR, N. (1988) 'School mathematics theorems – an endless source of surprise', *For the Learning of Mathematics,* **8**(3), pp. 34–40.

THE OPEN UNIVERSITY (1985) PM641 *Routes to/Roots of Algebra*, Milton Keynes, Open University Press.

PIRIE, S. and SCHWARZENBERGER, R. (1988) 'Mathematical discussion and understanding', *Educational Studies in Mathematics,* **19**(4), pp. 459–70.

THE PRIME PROJECT (1991) *Calculators, Children and Mathematics*, London, Simon and Schuster.

ROSENTHAL, R. and JACOBSEN, L. (1968) *Pygmalion in the Classroom*, London, Holt, Rhinehart and Winston.

SACKS, O. (1986) 'The twins' in *The Man who Mistook his Wife for a Hat*, London, Picador/Pan Books.

SCHOOL MATHEMATICS PROJECT (SMP) (1983) *Formulas: extension 1,* SMP 11–16, Cambridge, Cambridge University Press.

SCHOOLS COUNCIL (1977) *Mixed-ability Teaching in Mathematics*, London, Evans/Methuen Educational.

SCOTT, H. (1990) 'Understanding understanding', *Mathematics Teaching,* **132**, pp. 17–20.

SHULMAN, L. (1986) 'Those who understand: knowledge growth in teaching', *Educational Researcher,* **15**(2), pp. 4–14.

SKEMP, R. (1979) *Intelligence, Learning and Action: a foundation for theory and practice*, London, Wiley.

SMITH, J. (1988) 'Questioning questioning', *Mathematics Teaching,* **115**, p. 47.

TAHTA, D. (1981) 'Some thoughts arising from the new Nicolet films', *Mathematics Teaching,* **94**, pp. 25–9.

TAHTA, D. (1985) 'Imagery: geometry and number' in WADDINGHAM, J. and WIGLEY, A. (eds) *Secondary Mathematics with the Micro: in-service pack*, MEP, p. 5.

THOMPSON, A. (1984) 'The relationship of teachers' conceptions of mathematics and mathematics teaching to instructional practice', *Educational Studies in Mathematics,* **15**, pp. 105–27.

WALKERDINE, V. (1988) *The Mastery of Reason: cognitive development and the production of rationality*, London, Routledge.

WIGLEY, A., ROOKE, D., HART, M. and BELL, A., (1981) *Algebra,* Nottingham, South Notts Project, Shell Centre for Mathematical Education, University of Nottingham.

WOOD, D.G., BRUNER, J.S. and ROSS, G. (1976) 'The role of tutoring in problem solving', *Journal of Child Psychology and Psychiatry,* **17**(2), pp. 89-100.

WELFORD, A.T. (1987) 'Human skill' in GREGORY, R.L. (ed.) *The Oxford Companion to the Mind*, Oxford, Oxford University Press, pp. 715–6.